Stars in the Making

THE HARVARD BOOKS ON ASTRONOMY
Edited by
HARLOW SHAPLEY and BART J. BOK

ATOMS, STARS, and NEBULAE
Leo Goldberg and Lawrence H. Aller

THE MILKY WAY
Bart J. Bok and Priscilla F. Bok

TELESCOPES AND ACCESSORIES
George Z. Dimitroff and James G. Baker

GALAXIES
Harlow Shapley

OUR SUN
Donald H. Menzel

THE STORY OF VARIABLE STARS
Leon Campbell and Luigi Jacchia

BETWEEN THE PLANETS
Fletcher G. Watson

EARTH, MOON, and PLANETS
F. L. Whipple

Stars in
the Making

BY CECILIA PAYNE-GAPOSCHKIN
Phillips Astronomer, Harvard University

HARVARD UNIVERSITY PRESS · CAMBRIDGE · 1952

Library of Congress Catalog Card Number 52–9378
Printed in the United States of America

TO MY YOUNGEST SON

PETER JOHN ARTHUR

PREFACE

A series of lectures, delivered at the Lowell Institute in Boston, led to this book. The interest and stimulation of the audience encouraged me to put the material into more permanent form.

If any astronomer chances to read what I have written, he may deplore the sins of commission, but his own experience will, I hope, incline him to excuse the sins of omission, and the popular form in which I have expressed technical results.

My gratitude is due to Dr. Walter Baade for epistolary discussion of many problems concerning galaxies. I express my warm thanks to Dr. Harlow Shapley for reading and discussing the manuscript, and to Mr. J. D. Elder, of the Harvard University Press, for his editorial help and advice. Especial thanks are due to Dr. Bart J. Bok, whose care in reading these chapters, interest in discussion of the problems that they expose, and generosity in providing photographs for illustration, have far overstepped the obligations of an editor. I am grateful also to Miss Sybil L. Chubb for her skilful typing of the manuscript.

The verse on page 151 is from James Elroy Flecker, "A New Year's Carol," and is quoted by permission of Martin Secker and Warburg, Ltd., the publishers.

C. P.-G.

Contents

Introduction

Cosmic Evolution

The man who presumes to talk of the evolution of the stars must needs be an optimist with a sense of humor. And astronomers are incorrigible optimists. They peer up through a turbulent ocean of atmosphere at the stars and galaxies, forever inaccessible. They speak of million-degree temperatures, of densities smaller than our lowest vacuum; they study light that left its source two hundred million years ago. From a fleeting glimpse they reconstruct a whole history.

The study of cosmic evolution is perhaps the most daring flight of human imagination. For the universe seems changeless. Day succeeds day, the steady rhythm of the seasons moves against the background of the unchanging stars. Hipparchus made a record of the constellations two thousand years ago, and the same figures look down on us today. The Dipper and Orion were as familiar to Homer as they are to us. The Zodiac, the path of the Sun's march among the stars, was divided by the ancient Babylonians into figures whose very names were the forerunners of those we use. Recorded history, which has witnessed the change and decay of civilizations, furnishes no evidence, gives no hint, of changes in the nature of the stars.

And yet, as we shall see, the stars are changing. The drama of cosmic evolution is played out upon a stage that stretches beyond the limits of our vision, at a pace so slow that the span of human history has witnessed no action.

None the less, evidences of the drama are spread before us. We are like people who stand outside a movie theater, and try to reconstruct the story from a display of single "shots." The telescope furnishes a tantalizing array of "still pictures" that show the protagonists of the cosmic drama grouped in a variety of situations and attitudes. Each "still" represents the interplay of a group of actors. We witness individuals in moments of crisis, and individuals that radiate tranquillity. Intimate scenes pass before us, groupings that reveal crucial moments of the drama. Stupendous mob scenes reveal the tendencies of stellar communities. The task of astronomy is to analyze the interplay of forces that has produced each situation, and to weave the situations into a coherent drama.

I can but present the story as I see it. I may have misinterpreted some of the pictures. Some crucial situations may be missing. But, despite the size of the stage and the slowness of the action, I seem to discern the main thread of the story.

The first two chapters introduce the actors. Many of the great stars are already familiar; but those in the supporting roles carry an equally important share of the action. And a host of characters, so minor that we recognize them only as members of a crowd, are the real masters of the situation.

The three chapters that follow will analyze the "still pictures": first intimate situations, then stellar mob scenes, and finally the huge panoramas in which the whole stage is exposed to view, all characters caught at one dramatic moment.

In the three final chapters the situations are woven into a drama. The first of them is of the nature of a prologue, which sets the stage by flashbacks that build up the situation. Then follows the story of the slow development of the great stellar communities. Last of all comes the analysis of the actors, great and small — the growth of their characters, their interplay, their ultimate fate.

The attempt to tell the story of the cosmic drama may well seem to call for unexampled temerity. It far outruns the critical analysis of single situations, and presumes to generalize from a glance at a few "stills" — pitifully few and inadequately recorded. Astronomy dares, in the words of the mystic:

> *To see a world in a grain of sand*
> *And a heaven in a wild flower,*
> *Hold infinity in the palm of your hand*
> *And eternity in an hour.*

PART ONE

THE PLAYERS

1   Stars

Five thousand stars are visible to the unaided eye; a four-inch lens reveals over two million; and over a billion are accessible with the 200-inch mirror. The fainter we go, the more rapidly do the numbers increase. The story is told that Edward C. Pickering, of Harvard, was describing a formula that expressed the number of stars brighter than any given magnitude.* One of his hearers remarked that the formula required *two* stars brighter than apparent magnitude −1, whereas there is only one such star — Sirius. "Ah!" said Pickering, "*You've forgotten the sun.*" Perhaps familiarity breeds contempt; it is easy to forget that the sun is the nearest of the stars, the most readily studied, the only one that can be kept under continuous surveillance.

The sun is a typical star, a common kind of star. A quarter million stars have been analyzed in some detail, and 10 percent of them resemble the sun; it merely happens that most of them are far away, and our luminary is near by. A typical specimen of the cosmic population is, so to speak, on our doorstep — giving us a superb opportunity to study the construction and habits of stars in general.

The Light of the Sun. — The sun is a gigantic globe of glowing gas, and so is every star that shines, though not one other is near enough to appear as a disk, even to the most powerful telescope.†

* Magnitude is the astronomer's measure of stellar brightness — a logarithmic scale in which the smaller numbers express the greater brightness. A difference of one magnitude corresponds to a ratio in brightness of 2½.

† The planets that move round the sun are distinguished from stars by the facts that they do show disks in the telescope, and that they do not shine by their own light — they merely reflect sunlight. All the stars that we observe, on the other hand, are self-luminous — they are so hot that their surfaces glow.

With over a hundred times the diameter of our planet, more than a million times its bulk, three hundred thousand times its mass, the sun is yet a small star and a lightweight. The dazzling surface, intolerable to the eye even at a distance of 93 million miles, many times brighter than the most powerful artificial light, pales in comparison to those of the hottest stars. Yet, in its degree, the sun displays the same capacities as other stars; close-ups of its face reveal nuances of expression that elude us at greater distances, and provide clues to the behavior of the other members of the cosmic population.

We take the steady dependability of sunlight for granted in everyday life, and not without reason. The most careful measurement has revealed only infinitesimal variations during the past half-century, and most of these have probably been caused by variations in the transparency of our own atmosphere.

The earth's temperature is almost entirely governed by the amount of heat received from the sun, and the very fact that life on earth has existed in unbroken sequence for hundreds of millions of years shows that *the sun has been shining steadily at least as long as that*. The earth receives energy at the rate of 4,690,000 horsepower per square mile from the sun, and has been doing so for hundreds of millions of years, and yet our tiny planet intercepts less than two thousand-millionths of the sun's radiated energy. Such numbers beggar the imagination.

Put in another way, the output of the sun is even more impressive. Modern physics recognizes not only the interconvertibility of various forms of energy, but also the equivalence of energy and mass. The famous Einstein equation states that

$$E = mc^2,$$

where E is the energy in ergs, m the mass in grams, and c the speed of light, 3×10^{10} centimeters, or about 186,000 miles, per second.*

---

* The gram is the physicist's unit of mass, the mass of a cubic centimeter of water under standard conditions: 1000 grams = 2.205 lb, or 1 gram = 0.03527 oz avoirdupois = 0.03215 oz troy. An erg is the amount of energy required to lift 1/980 gram of matter one centimeter — a very small unit. About 40 million ergs equal one calorie (the amount of heat required to raise the temperature of 1 gram of water under standard conditions by 1 centigrade degree).

In the sense of this equation, light has weight just as matter does. The sun pours *four million tons* of radiant energy into space every second, and if (as we believe) this has been going on for at least a hundred million years, more than 10,000,000,000,000,000,000,000 (or 10^{22}) tons of light and heat have issued from our luminary in a steady stream! Large as the figure is, it represents less than one millionth of the total mass of the sun. As we shall see, the sun is actually converting its own substance into radiant energy. But it draws upon less than one million-millionth of its material capital a year — a very modest expenditure. Many stars are far more prodigal of their resources.

The Surface of the Sun. — The sun's steady output suggests tranquillity, but its surface is far from quiescent. Dark spots on it are often visible to the naked eye, and a completely unspotted sun is extremely rare (Plate 1). Closer scrutiny reveals a continually changing fine granulation over the entire disk. The sun's face is not a smooth unruffled sea of gas, but a heaving, churning expanse, with whirling tornadoes (sunspots) that break through from below, tongues of gas (spicules) that surge up and subside, clouds of glowing vapor (prominences) that float, swirl, and erupt high above the surface, and sudden localized blazes of intensely brilliant radiation (flares) (Plate 4). On the sun these things can be seen; on the stars they can only be surmised or indirectly observed, but we can be sure that they are often even more spectacular than on the sun.

The whole surface of the sun — flares, granulations, even sunspots — glows with intense brilliance. A complete array of color * is present, from x-rays through the visible spectrum to radio waves, and perhaps it is no coincidence that the sun shines most brightly in the colors to which our eyes are sensitive. The fact that the sun is brightest in the yellow-green gives a clue to the temperature of its radiating surface. Common experience tells that the hotter a glowing surface, the bluer is the light by which it shines; and the quantitative formulation of this fact (Wien's law) enables us to say that the

* Light is only a small section of the spectrum of electromagnetic radiation. X-rays, ultraviolet rays, light, infrared, microwaves, radio waves are all of the same nature, differ only in the length of the wave.

radiating surface of the sun has a temperature of about 6000°C (11,000°F). And this is true whatever the sun is made of.

The Composition of the Sun. — The brightness of the sun is not distributed among all colors with unbroken brilliance. When sunlight is passed through a prism, and spread into the artificial rainbow known as the *spectrum,* some colors are seen to be greatly depleted. The rainbow is broken up into an array of sharply bounded regions of color, separated by others, far less brilliant (the "Fraunhofer lines"). Something has robbed the sunlight of these colors, and the atoms above the solar surface have been convicted as the culprits (Plate 18).

Each atom has its own characteristic array of colors, and it can take up or give out these colors only, absorbing or emitting energy as it does so. The distribution of the colors in sunlight, and our knowledge of the behavior of atoms on earth, make possible a chemical analysis of the sun's surface, actually more delicate than we could perform in the laboratory if we had a chunk of the sun given us to analyze.* The results of the analysis show that the sun is made of the familiar chemical elements known on earth.

The matching of characteristic colors led at first to a qualitative analysis, and showed that *all* known atoms with spectrum lines in the accessible region of the sun † are represented in its spectrum. A few simple compounds, such as cyanogen, are found, but most of the material is in the form of isolated atoms. In other words, the spectrum shows that *the outer layers of the sun are completely gaseous.* One can go further: the array of colors characteristic of an atom varies with temperature, and so the temperature of the low-lying atmosphere of the sun, which produces the Fraunhofer lines, can be determined; it agrees fairly well with the temperature inferred from the color of sunlight.

Growing knowledge of the physics of spectra has actually made it possible not only to identify the atoms above the sun's surface, but

* This is because of the great depth of the layer of atoms above the sun's surface, and the vast number accordingly available for the analysis. A large number of spectrum lines, only *predictable* on earth, can actually be *observed* in the spectrum of the sun!

† Molecules in the atmosphere of the earth, especially those of ozone, oxygen, and water vapor, obscure some parts of the sun's spectrum almost completely.

6

to count them. The sun, we find, is mainly hydrogen; there are more atoms of hydrogen, lightest and simplest of atoms, than of all other kinds put together. Next in order comes the second lightest atom, helium, and, with some notable exceptions, the numbers of heavier, more complex atoms fall off steadily in order of complexity.

This scheme of chemical composition is not peculiar to the sun. It is typical of the composition of the whole cosmos, not only the stars, but also the loose gas and dust that pervade interstellar space. The atomic makeup of all stars is not identical — and the differences, small as they are, may be of great significance — but the general uniformity is amazing, and it would be difficult to point with confidence to any cosmic object that does not consist mainly of hydrogen.

The Sun's Surface. — Each atom has its characteristic array of colors, and a photograph of the sun in a single color records the atoms of one kind by themselves. Luckily the sun is so bright that even a very restricted range of color can be photographed, either with the instrument known as a spectroheliograph or by an ingenious arrangement of light filters. Pictures of the sun made by the light of calcium or hydrogen show not only increased detail, but revealingly different detail (Plate 3). Whereas a direct photograph, in light of all colors, shows only dark sunspots and vague granulations, calcium light reveals brilliant variegations in the neighborhood of the sunspots, and greatly accentuates the contrast of the granulation. Even before a sunspot swirls through the surface, bright calcium "flocculi" herald its presence; and they remain for some time to mark the place after the spot has died away. The bright areas shown by the calcium atoms reflect the greater disturbances, more violent motions, and probably hotter regions, near the tornadoes that are sunspots.

Hydrogen poses are more difficult to take, because hydrogen does not cut so wide a swath in the spectrum as calcium, and less light is available for the photograph. This may seem surprising, for there is much more hydrogen than calcium above the sun's surface; but it is a consequence of the idiosyncrasies of the two kinds of atoms. At the sun's temperature nearly all the calcium atoms are in the right state to emit light, but the atom of hydrogen is more recalcitrant,

7

and is only about one-millionth as prone to emit as calcium at 6000°C. Hydrogen atoms are more than ten thousand times as common as atoms of calcium, but even so, the lines they produce in the spectrum of the sun are less than one-hundredth as intense.

Photographs in hydrogen light (Plate 4) show the disturbed regions near sunspots, but with less brilliance, because of the difficulty of stimulating the atoms. Both the hydrogen and the calcium photographs reveal slowly changing patterns of dark filaments silhouetted against the bright surface of the sun. The filaments are not really dark; they seem so only by contrast. When one of them extends beyond the sun's edge it is seen as a glowing prominence — a great cloud of gas poised above the surface (Plate 5). Some prominences are so brilliant that they show up as bright streaks, even against the face of the sun.

Prominences are protean in form (Plates 6 and 7), and have an infinite variety of motions. Some hang poised over the surface. Some spurt upward, in filamentary surges, like geysers, and seem to dissipate into space. Some rise and fall like fountains. But a surprising majority shower downward, not upward, and many give the impression of being sucked into a point at the surface.

We are far from understanding the motions of prominences. Some are associated with sunspots, but many are not. The variegated brilliance of the sun's surface may affect them. Electric forces may be of importance; magnetic forces probably play a crucial role. Whatever be the significant factors in producing the protean variety of solar prominences, they are important also in stars of very different kinds. For, as we shall see, prominence activity is characteristic of many stars, and often on a scale that makes the sun's activities seem puny.

Whether or not the motions of prominences are governed by magnetic forces, very intense magnetic fields are observed on the sun. The spectrum of a sunspot tells the story, through the medium of the spectra of the individual atoms in the tornado. An atom in a magnetic field absorbs and radiates in a special way; its peculiar series of colors subdivides into an intricate pattern, and the stronger the magnetic field, the more is the subdivision accentuated. The sunspot behaves like a tremendous electromagnet, many thousand

8

miles across; no doubt electrically charged particles, whirling around the axis of the tornado, play the part of the current in the electromagnet, and a powerful magnetic field is produced along the axis of the spot. Sunspots, like prominences, are incompletely understood, but that they possess magnetic fields of several thousand gauss * is certain. Large as such fields are, even larger magnetic fields are found for certain peculiar stars *as a whole*; and like many sunspots, they reverse their polarity at regular intervals.

The times when sunspots are thickly scattered over the sun's face are marked by striking events nearer home. The Aurorae, the Northern Lights, gleam and shimmer in the sky. Magnetic storms disrupt communications and intrude on radio programs. The disturbances that produce spots on the sun have direct effects on our planet.

Disturbed areas of the sun are showering particles into space at high speeds, and a rain of electrons, protons, and even heavier particles pours down into our atmosphere. An electrically charged shower plays upon the atoms and molecules of the upper air, and excites the auroral glow. Oxygen in the high atmosphere emits its peculiar red and green light; molecules of nitrogen and other substances contribute their characteristic colors. The spectrum of the rain of solar hydrogen has recently been photographed by Meinel. The earth receives showers of particles that left the sun a few hours † ago. Even more significant: the sun is continually spraying matter into space. Many stars, as we shall see, are doing the same.

Prominences are not the only features that rise above the sun's bright edge. At the crucial moment of a total eclipse, when the moon's disk cuts off the body of the sun, a brilliant rim of rosy light — the chromosphere — appears around it. The spectrum of the chromosphere shows that it consists of radiating atoms, the same atoms that were revealed by the Fraunhofer lines in a layer nearer the sun's surface, but with a difference. The pattern of colors that they radiate is modified in a way that admits of but one explanation — the temperature of the chromosphere, from five to ten thousand

* The gauss is the unit of magnetic field. The magnetic field of the earth, which affects the compass, is small — a fraction of a gauss.

† The particles travel at 125 to 625 miles a second, and make the trip from sun to earth in from 200 to 40 hours.

miles above the solar surface, is more than three times the temperature of the atoms that produce the absorption spectrum of the sun! Even helium, which is far more refractory than hydrogen, and requires a far higher temperature to excite it, appears not only in normal form, but even in the "ionized" condition, with one electron torn away — a situation found only at the surfaces of the hottest stars, at temperatures of over 30,000°C.

The chromosphere consists of a sort of hairy rim of tiny spicules, or jets, which spurt upward and disappear in a few minutes. The spicules may be related to the minute granules that pepper the face of the sun, and seem equally short-lived.

Other stars than the sun possess chromospheres, and with some of them, unlike the sun, the chromosphere is far larger than the star itself, and shines so brilliantly that the glowing atoms in the spectrum produce *bright spectrum lines* on the background of the star's light. Some chromospheres are poised, like the sun's, above the star's surface, with little motion. The shining atoms around other stars are flowing or spurting steadily outward, and some stars occasionally blow great chromospheric bubbles, which thin out gradually and dissipate into space.

Outside the chromosphere of the sun gleam the pearly streamers of the corona (Plate 8), which extend to distances comparable to the size of the sun itself. Like the chromosphere, the corona has a spectrum given by glowing atoms, but for many years its nature was a mystery. No such colors had been produced by any atoms on earth, and they used to be ascribed to a mysterious substance, *coronium*, that was unknown elsewhere. Now we know, from the work of the Swedish physicist Edlén, that the corona consists of well-known, common elements (such as iron, calcium, and nickel) but under conditions that represent temperatures never attained on earth (Plate 9). The corona — the "iron crown" of the sun — seems to be at a temperature of about a million degrees!

Other stars, too, have coronas, and some of them are intensely brilliant. The spectral colors of the sun's iron crown have been found in the light of certain peculiar stars that have suffered sudden explosion.

Perhaps the most remarkable thing about the outer regions of the sun is the increasing temperature of successive outward layers. The reversing layer and the photosphere * have temperatures of about 6000°; the chromosphere is at about 20,000°; and the corona, at 1,000,000°. The sunspots, which look like depressions in the solar surface, are even cooler than the reversing layer; their spectra and colors point to a temperature not far from 4000°.

The remarkable temperature stratification of the sun is not an isolated phenomenon. Other stars show it, and some of them display an even greater span of conditions. If we did not know that the sun is a single star, the variety of its spectra might tempt us to doubt; other stars whose spectra look as though they must be complex may be similarly put together.

The Sun's Rotation. — From the human point of view, the most important thing about the sun is the fact that it has planets, and that one of them presents physico-chemical conditions favorable to life. But from the standpoint of the sun, all the planets are negligible: even Jupiter, the largest, weighs less than one thousand as much as our luminary. Within the planetary system, Jupiter is the only really influential member; it is the most potent factor, for example, in governing the motions of the comets and asteroids, the lesser members of the system. In one respect, Jupiter excels even the sun: the giant planet possesses most of the total energy of rotation of the solar system — far more than the sun itself. True, the sun is spinning, but spinning very slowly. It takes nearly a month to make one complete turn. This fact has always been one of the great difficulties in the path of a theory of the origin of the solar system; almost all the theories that have been moderately successful in other ways seem to require that the sun possess the greater part of the energy of rotation of the whole.

The slow spinning of the sun is far from being unusual. Most stars that resemble the sun in size and temperature are also turning slowly on their axes. Some stars, it is true, spin very rapidly, but these are usually the massive stars of high temperature. Stars such as the sun rotate rapidly only when constrained to do so by being

* The photosphere, or "sphere of light," is the glowing surface of the sun; the reversing layer is the atmosphere of absorbing atoms that lies above it. Temperatures, here and later, are given on the centigrade scale.

11

members of twin systems; they raise huge tides in each other and always stay face to face. Any star that spins rapidly is distorted into a spheroid; even the solid or semisolid planets like the earth, Jupiter, and Saturn are more or less flattened at the poles by rotation. Jupiter looks like an orange, even in a small telescope. But the sun is so nearly spherical that no polar flattening has ever been detected.

Slowly as the sun rotates, it still does so in a remarkable manner: it spins faster at the equator than at the poles, so that its surface must be in a state of shear — that is, some parts of the surface must continually be slipping past others. Possibly the differential rotation plays some part in producing sunspot vortexes. And if even the slowly turning sun spins faster at the equator than at the poles, what of the stars that turn on themselves in a few hours, and are highly distorted? What, too, of the internal rotation of the sun? We can see the surface only; and a different internal rate of rotation is not only possible but likely. A star that turns very slowly will probably not churn up its interior and mix its constituents; but one that is spinning fast may be much better mixed. The degree of mixing of the materials within a star may well be a crucial factor in its history.

The Sun's Interior. — Which brings us to the problem of the sun's interior. So far we have spoken only of the parts of the sun that can be seen, a mere skin. Conditions within are very different. Without going beyond the elementary laws of physics, it can be shown that the sun, and all other stars, are gaseous not only at the surface, but all the way through. Moreover, both temperature and pressure must necessarily rise toward the center.

In fact, it is well known that the central temperature of a star must depend essentially on its size and mass, and is proportional to the average mass of the individual particles of which it consists. This average mass of the particles, the so-called "mean molecular weight," would be least for a star that was all made of hydrogen, and would increase somewhat — but not very much — with larger proportions of heavier elements. The reason for this rather surprising statement is that *the interiors of the stars are so hot that atoms are stripped of nearly all their electrons.* Each electron counts as one particle in the average mass of the individual particles, and the masses of electrons are negligible, even in comparison with those

12

of the nuclei * of hydrogen, lightest of elements. In units of the hydrogen nucleus, a star all of hydrogen would have a "mean molecular weight" of ½; if the star were all helium, whose nucleus weighs four times as much as hydrogen, and which can part with two electrons, the average molecular weight would be ⅘, or 1.33; even if the stars were all uranium (92 electrons, atomic weight 238 times hydrogen), the mean molecular weight would only be $^{238}\!/_{93}$, or 2.55. As most stars consist mainly of hydrogen, the mean molecular weight will usually be between ½ and 1½; and the central temperature, for stars of the same mass and size but different composition, will therefore not differ by a factor of more than 2 or 3.

If, in addition to size and mass, the total energy output (luminosity) of a star is known, the same elementary theory permits the calculation of the mean molecular weight, which can be fitted by a certain number of different combinations of hydrogen, helium, and heavier elements.

The sun is found to have a central temperature near to 18 million degrees; and the temperature almost certainly increases steadily from the surface inward. Thus we have the odd paradox that the sun is actually coolest at the surface, or even a little below it, in the cores of the sunspots, and the temperature goes up again as we pass outward through the chromosphere to the corona.

High temperature and enormous pressure prevail within the sun. The high temperature is responsible for the fact that the sun's substance behaves like an ideal gas, even at the center; it strips the atoms of their attendant electrons, resolves them into fragments far smaller than at the surface, and permits them to pack more closely without violating the laws that govern the behavior of gases.

The Sun's Source of Energy. — The hot interior of the sun is the source of its light and heat. At 18 million degrees the atoms are able to interact, to convert some of their substance into energy. No other source is adequate to have produced the tremendous outpouring, steady over millions of years. The source of the sun's energy was

* Atoms, so named because they were once thought to be indivisible, are complex bodies. Most of their mass resides in the central core, or *nucleus*, around which hovers a haze of electrons. These electrons give the atom its chemical properties, and most of its physical properties also.

13

long a puzzle. Combustion, chemical reaction, gravitational contraction, the drawing of energy from the environment, all were shown to be hopelessly inadequate. Nuclear energy seemed the only avenue of salvation, long before the details of the actual process were understood. "Does energy issue freely from matter," speculated Eddington a quarter of a century ago, "at 40 million degrees as steam issues from water at 100 degrees?"

Modern nuclear physics provides an affirmative answer. The actual processes have been observed in the laboratory. The interior of the sun liberates energy by a catalytic action similar to those of atomic chemistry; but the reactants are the naked nuclei, not atoms clad in their haze of electrons. Hans Bethe and C. F. von Weiszäcker discovered independently, nearly at the same time, that hydrogen cores combine, by a chain of reactions set off by carbon nuclei; four hydrogens interlock to produce a helium core. The helium is lighter than the sum of the hydrogens by about 0.7 percent, and this deficiency of mass is turned into energy, which passes from the interior to the surface in a steady flow. Only at temperatures between 15 and 20 million degrees can the reaction produce enough energy to supply the sun. The rate of production varies as about the eighteenth power of the temperature, and most of the sun's energy accordingly issues from its substance in the central region where the temperature is highest. At 15 million degrees the "light" given out resembles x-rays (even more "violet" than ultraviolet light); it flows outward, passed from hand to hand, so to speak, by the electrons and atoms of the overlying layers, and is steadily "reddened" in the process so that when it reaches the surface the observable color is primarily yellow-green.*

The sun shines by feeding on its own substance, and its diet is exceedingly simple. So far as we know, our luminary subsists entirely upon hydrogen. The same food sustains the other stars; stellar infants may possibly have a somewhat different diet, but their infancy is brief, if only because foods other than hydrogen are in short

* Actually the sun's surface gives out a surprising amount of radiation of very short wavelength, far more than would be expected if its light were distributed according to the elementary laws of radiation by a so-called "black body" (a technical term, which sounds rather paradoxical, and denotes a surface that absorbs and radiates ideally according to certain laws that are deducible from quantum theory.)

supply. Digestive processes may differ somewhat from one kind of star to another. If the temperature is well below 15 million degrees, the cycle catalyzed by carbon may be replaced by others, such as the *direct* combination of protons (hydrogen nuclei) to form helium — the "proton-proton" reaction. The food remains the same; hydrogen is consumed and helium is left behind.

Although the sun has been steadily digesting its own interior for tens, and even for thousands, of millions of years, it still consists almost entirely of hydrogen, enough to keep things going at the present rate for at least an equal interval. Most other stars are equally rich in the vital substance, and have an equally bright future. In fact, paradoxically enough, the future of stars that are consuming hydrogen is even brighter than their past. For the brightness of a star of given size and mass depends primarily on the mean molecular weight of its substance. As the hydrogen supply slowly falls, the mean molecular weight gradually increases, and the star grows a little brighter, so long as it does not drastically alter its internal arrangements.

The great astronomer Eddington showed, even before the actual process of stellar nutrition was identified, that the more massive a star is, the more energy does it pour out. The energy output of a star of given composition is, in fact, proportional to something between the cube and the fourth power of its mass. The greater majority of the stars whose masses are known conform to this rule (the "mass-luminosity law") fairly closely. Most of the differences are within the limits that would be expected from the possible range of mean molecular weight with composition — a range that was shown earlier to involve a factor not greater than two or three. But some stars, as we shall see later, are nonconformists, and they are important finger posts for theories of stellar evolution.

If a star's luminosity (which can be expressed in terms of tons of radiation per second for all stars, just as for the sun) were simply proportional to its mass, all stars of similar composition would have the same life expectancy. But a star much more massive than the sun is consuming itself much faster. A star of twice the mass is twelve times as prolific; at ten times the mass the factor is over a thousand, and at a hundred times the mass of the sun a star would be well over

15

a million times as prodigal, and its life expectancy a million times shorter. The total life of a star like the sun (in the style to which we are accustomed) is about 5000 million years; if there were stars a hundred times as massive, their active lives would be reckoned in thousands rather than in millions of years, and they must become effectively bankrupt during an interval over which the sun can radiate with virtually unchanging brightness.

Such bankrupt stars actually exist. They can be recognized by the fact that their brightness is far lower than we should expect from the mass-luminosity law. Their light is feeble; they have exhausted their internal nuclear resources, have spent all their available hydrogen, and exist only on their very limited gravitational capital.* Such a destiny probably awaits all stars, but for most of them it lies in the far future. Even for the sun we see it as inevitable.

The sun, indeed, holds a mirror to the cosmos. Like all other stars it is a globe of glowing gas, hotter and denser within. Its surface is a seething, surging sea of atoms. Plumes of gas float above it; glowing filaments surge upward; shining fountains cascade downward. Giant tornadoes swirl through the surface. Spicules rise and dissipate like darting flames. Dazzling flares blaze up and vanish. A brilliant chromosphere rings it; and around it gleams the aura of the corona. Powerful magnetic forces play across the surface; atoms and electrons spray into space. As it spins on its axis the equator pulls steadily ahead; and across its face proceeds the slow rhythm of the sunspot cycle, waxing and waning every eleven years. The spectacle is impressive in itself. As the mirror of the cosmos it is stupendous. Other stars are doing the same things, and these stellar habits are the clue to their history.

The sun is made of hydrogen, "with a smell of other substances," † and so are most other stars. The steady consumption of hydrogen keeps it shining; most stars are sustained in no other way. Wherever we look in the cosmos we see the play of the same forces, the march of the same phenomena — but often on a scale that makes the sun seem puny. Let us turn to the stars, and compare the other members of the caste with the player whom we brought first upon the stage.

* A star can convert gravitational energy into light and heat by contracting in size.
† Rosseland.

16

Orion and the Dog Stars. — The constellations come down to us from remote antiquity. The very names by which we call Orion, the mighty hunter, and the Dog Star, Sirius, are the ones by which Homer knew them. They shine in the winter sky, beside the Milky Way, Orion resplendent with belt and sword, the Great Dog at his side, the Lesser Dog behind.

Sirius, the Dog Star, is by far the brightest in the night sky. Its brilliance is deceptive, a consequence of its being one of the nearest stars to us, but it is nevertheless among the brighter stars, about forty times as bright as the sun.* It is about twice as large, weighs about twice as much, and is nearly twice as hot at the surface. Stars like Sirius are fairly common (though less so than stars like the sun); Vega, for example, has about the same size, brightness, weight, and temperature.

Sirius has, however, a distinction that Vega lacks; it is attended by another much fainter star, sometimes irreverently called "the Pup" (Fig. 1). The two move around one another in elliptical orbits under their mutual gravitational pull. The "Pup" is about as massive as the sun and rather hotter at the surface, but it is a little more than 3 percent of the size, and only about 2 percent as bright. Here is a flagrant exception to the rule that the luminosity of a star depends on its mass; if the "Pup" conformed to the mass-luminosity law it would be over fifty times as bright as it is. The "Pup," in fact, is a stellar bankrupt that has consumed all the available hydrogen fuel, and seems to be shining only by dint of slowly shrinking, and thus converting gravitational energy into light. Although it weighs nearly as much as the sun, it has only about one twenty-five-thousandth of the volume, and its substance is so closely packed that *a cubic inch of it would weigh a ton.* Amazingly enough, it is nonetheless gaseous throughout — composed of matter in the so-called degenerate state, incapable of yielding energy except by contraction. This star, more formally named the "companion of Sirius," was the first stellar

* Sirius does not, of course, *look* forty times as bright as the sun to us, because it is so much farther away. If it were placed where the sun is, its light would seem to us forty times as brilliant as the sun's. In comparing the brightness, or *luminosity,* of stars, an astronomer lines them up, in imagination, all at the same distance, and states how their luminosities would compare. The brightness at a standard distance is known as the *absolute luminosity* or the *absolute magnitude.*

17

bankrupt to be discovered, and is one of the nearest and best observed of this group of stars, which are known as the "white dwarfs."

Amazing as its character is, the companion of Sirius is far from
unique. Among the twenty-five stars nearest to the sun (and hence
to us) there are three white dwarfs, and only one star like Sirius. Almost two hundred white dwarfs are known, largely through the work
of Luyten. If we make due allowance for the fact that white dwarfs

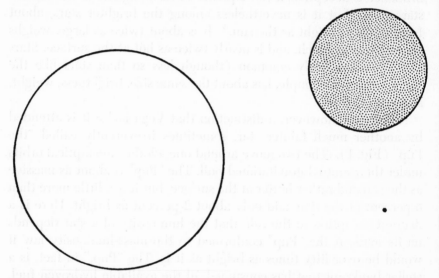

FIG. 1. *Sirius and its companion, drawn to scale. The shaded circle represents the sun on the
same scale. In this and the other figures, shading is used to denote temperature: the more heavily
shaded is the star, the lower its temperature.*

are faint, inconspicuous, and hard to find, we realize that they may
well be five or even ten times as common as stars like Sirius. They
may even be commoner in our part of the cosmos than stars like the
sun. Sirius is actually a more exceptional star than its faint attendant,
even though its properties may seem to us less fantastic. In attempt-
ing to put together the story of stellar development, the white
dwarfs, amazing as their properties are, must be assigned essential
parts in the drama.

Procyon, the Little Dog Star, is intermediate between the sun
and Sirius in size, mass, brightness, and temperature, somewhat

closer to the sun in all these characters. It, too, has a white-dwarf companion, even smaller and fainter than the "Pup" — so faint, indeed, that we cannot portray it in nearly as much detail. A third nearby white dwarf, called "van Maanen's star" after its discoverer, is apparently a single star; it also is smaller and fainter than the companion of Sirius, with one seven-thousandth of the diameter of the sun, one ten-thousandth of its brightness. The smallest white dwarf known is about as large as the planet Mercury; most of them are between the earth and the planet Uranus in size. We shall meet the white dwarfs again in describing "still pictures" of stellar situations.

Stellar bankruptcies are so common that the circumstances leading to them must be of a very usual kind; we must inquire whether there is any way out from stellar insolvency. That, however, is part of the drama; in the present chapter we are but introducing the characters.

Sirius looks bright because it is fairly near to us, but most of the naked-eye stars in Orion are far brighter. Alnitam, "the Chain of Pearls," the central star of the giant's belt (Plates 10 and 11), is at least six hundred times as bright as the sun,* four times as hot at the surface, ten times as large, and perhaps twenty times as massive. Alnitam is typical of the blue stars in Orion; a number of these are twin systems. Even hotter are some of the little knot of stars that form the central star of Orion's sword, the famous "Trapezium," of which eight stars are visible, and some at least of these are themselves twin systems. The stars of the Trapezium are so hot that they excite a glow in the surrounding clouds of gas, the "Great Nebula in Orion" (Plate 23).

Still hotter and more brilliant are the members of a mighty pair of stellar twins in Canis Major, the Great Dog — UW Canis Majoris,† one of the brightest naked-eye eclipsing stars (Fig. 4). Perhaps five times the sun's temperature, thirty times its size, over twenty times as massive, and more than ten thousand times as

---

* Here, and elsewhere, I refer to the *true* or *absolute* luminosity of the star — the brightness it would appear to have if it were at the same distance from us as the sun.

† Like many thousands of other stars, this one varies in brightness. Such stars need distinctive names, which are assigned by attaching one or more letters to the Latin name of the constellation in which they lie.

19

bright, these are conspicuous actors in the drama of stellar development. But though they obtrude themselves upon us by their brilliance, such stars are very uncommon; for every one of them we find a thousand Siriuses, a hundred thousand suns.

Supergiant Stars. — Equally brilliant is the blue star Rigel at the giant's heel (Plates 10 and 11). It is about 20,000 times as bright as the sun, somewhat hotter than Sirius, and a great deal larger — perhaps fifteen times the size of the Dog Star. Here we have a star with an immense chromosphere, fitfully lighted up by something akin to prominences, and prominences so brilliant that the light of their hydrogen atoms shows up even against the background of the brilliant stellar surface. The delicate detail of the atomic lines shows that the atmosphere of Rigel is far more tenuous than the sun's. The mass of Rigel is unknown to us, but it can scarcely be less than forty times the sun's. And as Rigel is 20,000 times as luminous as the sun, and pours out about 80,000 million tons of light a second, it is wasting its substance 500 times as fast, and has a life expectancy proportionally smaller. If the sun's probable lifetime is 5000 million years, that of Rigel is only 10 million. In other words, if it had been shining for 10 million years, it would be bankrupt now. Rigel is very far from bankrupt; it is one of the more conspicuous stellar prodigals. We can but conclude that *it is less than 10 million years of age.*

Across the constellation from Rigel, the brilliant Betelgeuse flickers with a ruddy light (Plates 10 and 11). Halfway between Vega and Rigel in brightness, it is far cooler than either, with a surface temperature about one-half the sun's. It is one of the largest stars, about three hundred times the sun's size, less than a millionth of the sun's density. The light of Betelgeuse is inconstant; probably this tenuous star is vibrating, half-rhythmically, changing in size, possibly even in shape, as it does so. But despite its tenuity, Betelgeuse is a *star*, condensed at the center, cohering under gravity. Perhaps it has the body of a star comparable to Alnitam, surrounded by an enormously distended cool chromosphere. Churning motions can be detected in the envelope of Betelgeuse, and the light of calcium prominences appears in its spectrum. We may picture the solar prominences on a greatly expanded scale, interlacing to obscure completely the true surface of the star within.

Stars like Rigel and Betelgeuse are extraordinarily infrequent, so much so that we might be justified in leaving them out altogether in an attempt to delineate the normal stellar life history. They differ from most stars in prodigality of output; they are above the average in mass, they must be below the average in age. Superficially they differ enormously, but both seem to have exaggerated chromospheres — a feature often shown by stellar prodigals. They do not differ from the general run of stars in kind — only in degree.

Variable Stars. — Above the giant's shoulder is an inconspicuous star, U Orionis, one of the numerous group known as long-period variables. It is nearly as large as Betelgeuse, and rather cooler at the surface. Its brightness does not flicker irregularly, but appears to the eye to fluctuate rhythmically. About once a year it brightens by a factor of over a hundred.* At its brightest U Orionis is about one-tenth as bright as Betelgeuse, which makes it still a hundred times as bright as the sun. Almost certainly it performs a rhythmic vibration, or pulsation, as it fades and brightens. Details of its spectrum show that it is surrounded by a tenuous envelope of cool gases, such as we pictured for Betelgeuse; but the envelope is not so opaque as to conceal brilliant radiations of hydrogen and other atoms, which are most clearly seen as the star is brightening, and suggest a sort of inner chromosphere at a much higher temperature. We have more than a suspicion that the rhythm of the star's variation is accompanied by intermittent spurts and streams of atoms into the surrounding space, something like what happens on the sun, but on a far more gigantic scale. Like the sun, U Orionis displays a wider range of conditions than might be expected at the surface of one star. The spectrum gives evidence of chemical compounds, such as the oxides of titanium and zirconium (only possible at quite low temperatures), and of bright lines of hydrogen (expected at temperatures three times as high). When the star is faint, it is seen to be surrounded by a sort of nebula of iron atoms — iron under conditions of extreme diffuseness, probably a cloud of iron vapor that

* The change of brightness is real, but as seen by the eye it is illusory; the star grows cooler as it grows fainter and the maximum of light passes toward the infrared, out of the visible range. The real change of brightness in all colors together is by a factor of about two.

drifts off into space. Similar radiations are observed in the neighborhood of exploding stars, and cannot (so far as we know) appear save at considerable distances from the stellar surface.

Long-period variables are something of an enigma: but it is an enigma to which the sun provides a clue. A distended sun, rhythmically pulsating, with exaggerated chromosphere and enormous prominence activity, might add up to something that looked very like U Orionis.

In another constellation lies a star that carries the same enigma even further — the variable star Z Andromedae. Here again is a star that varies in brightness with fair regularity. Sometimes it brightens only slightly, at other times enormously, and with explosive violence, but always with a regular rhythm of about three years. Here again we find spectra of chemical compounds, clues to low temperature; here again we see an amazing variable bright-line spectrum, indicative of very high temperature indeed. The color of the star becomes bluer as it brightens, which it sometimes does with spectacular suddenness and range. The various spectra indicate a span of conditions from something like the surface of Betelgeuse, with a temperature near 3000°, to a state comparable to that of the solar corona, with a temperature of a million degrees.

The stars like Z Andromedae (for it represents a sizeable group) have conventionally been considered to be double — a cool star mated with a hot, explosive one. But almost all the ingredients are present in the sun. Intermittent, brilliant flares, and a very bright chromosphere and corona, could conspire to add up to just such a picture. A few features, not present in the sun, might be attributed to the far more tenuous stellar envelope. Some of the stars of this peculiar "symbiotic" group, if regarded as doubles, would be influencing each other's changes in a manner hard to picture; a single star with a great span of physical conditions presents fewer difficulties: and we actually know of such a star — the sun itself.

Other pulsating stars lie within the confines of Orion. They seem faint, for they are very distant, but the faintest of them is nearly a hundred times as bright as the sun. Some (the so-called RR Lyrae stars) vibrate rapidly, growing bright and dim with a regular rhythm of less than a day. Others vibrate once in a few days; pulsing variable stars are indeed found with periods all the way from a couple of hours to several years.

Some stars that vary in brightness do so because of periodic eclipses; but we are not now concerned with these. The vibrating stars are single, and possess a regular rhythm that is governed by their condition. The more luminous, the more diffuse is a star, the slower is its rhythm (or the longer its *period*). The rate is known to be closely associated with the star's density.

The rapidly varying pulsating stars (RR Lyrae stars, with periods less than a day) are little larger than the sun, though twice as hot and nearly a hundred times as bright. Stars that pulsate in periods between a day and fifty days (Cepheids) are from ten to a hundred times the size of the sun, from a hundred to ten thousand times as bright. Even more slowly than the Cepheids pulsate the long-period variables like U Orionis.

Variable stars seem less inhibited than the sun; they vibrate freely, and seem to spray atoms around them as they do so. The sun, if it executes vibrations of the sort, does so on such a modest scale that it has gone undetected. Or possibly the solar counterpart of stellar variability has merely gone unrecognized, and is represented by the intermittent flares, or even by the sunspot cycle. We do not know the causes of stellar vibration or of the sunspot cycle. No connection is apparent; but we cannot be certain that none exists.

The Wolf-Rayet Stars. — One of the most spectacular stars in the sky lies in the constellation of the Great Dog (o^2 Canis Majoris). It is perhaps as luminous as Alnitam, but may well have twice the surface temperature. Its spectrum gives evidence of a huge and brilliant chromosphere, for bright-line radiations outweigh all other atomic lines. The spectroscope gives evidence of violent motion, with showers of atoms spurting rapidly at speeds of several thousand miles a second. Matter is pouring either inward or outward in tremendous quantities and at immense velocity. Some of the atoms, which lie between us and the star, are certainly spurting upward from the surface. But when we recall the motions of solar prominences, we recognize the possibility that atoms may be cascading downward as well as upward. This star (a representative of

23

a small and fascinating group, the so-called Wolf-Rayet stars *) is evidently in a state of crisis. Even a star like Rigel, with its limited future, is likely to last longer without drastic change.

Dwarf Stars. — All the bright stars in Orion and the Dogs are far brighter than the sun, but these brilliant performers that have their names in lights are a small minority. The whole face of the constellation is covered with myriads of inconspicuous stars, the mainstay of the stellar population. Stars like Procyon are commoner than stars like Sirius; sunlike stars are commoner than stars like Procyon, but the great bulk of the stars are even further down the scale: smaller, fainter, cooler, and less massive than the sun (Fig. 2). These "main-sequence stars" have few spectacular traits, but, *mutatis mutandis*, they are very like the sun — they, too, are no doubt intermittently spotted, and possess chromospheres and coronas too faint to be seen in contrast to their total light. The only "solar" phenomenon that can sometimes be seen for the fainter ones is flare activity; a burst of light similar to a solar flare, on the surface of a star ten thousand times fainter, can more than double the star's total light. Such flares have recently been found on several very faint cool stars, and show that even here the same forces are at work.

The smallest, faintest stars known (exclusive of the white dwarfs) have about one tenth of the sun's size, one fifth of its mass, rather less than half its surface temperature, and less than one ten-thousandth of its brightness. If (as we believe) these stars conform to the mass-luminosity relation, and subsist on their internal hydrogen, their life expectancy very greatly exceeds that of the sun. They constitute the enormous bulk of the stellar population in our neighborhood, and in the story of stellar development their testimony carries the greatest weight. Their existence seems monotonous; save for occasional superficial flares, they do not vary in brightness. Except as members of pairs they may seem uninteresting. But in stellar evolution their role is more important than that of the rare and brilliant stars that obtrude themselves on our attention.

The slowly spinning sun is not noticeably distorted by its rotation. The bright stars of Orion present a different picture. Many of them, probably most of them, are spinning rapidly. The bright, high-

* Named after two astronomers who first studied them.

temperature π^5 Orionis, for example, is spinning so fast that it is distorted from spherical form, not merely into an oblate spheroid, like the planet Jupiter, but into an ellipsoid with *three* axes that

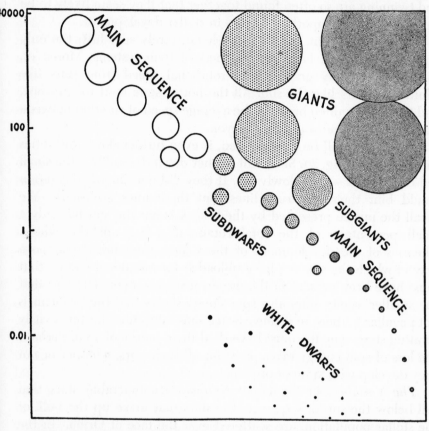

FIG. 2. *Typical stars, arranged so that the brightest are at the top of the figure, the coolest at the right. The various groups of stars that are mentioned in the text are illustrated by a few typical examples. The relative sizes of the stars are shown on a conventional scale; the largest stars shown are over a hundred thousand times as large as the smallest, but the circles give an idea of the distribution of size with brightness and temperature. The numbers on the left show the brightness of stars on the horizontal line, in terms of the brightness of the sun.*

differ. As it spins, it presents successively its larger and smaller profiles to us, and varies rhythmically in brightness — not by pulsations as the Cepheids do, but because it turns different sides successively toward us.

25

Most of the bright, high-temperature stars are spinning rapidly, and it is probably no coincidence that they are commonly found in pairs — twin stars that circle one another as they turn. Spinning and twinning are so often found together that they seem likely to be cause and effect, important factors in stellar development.

Stars like the sun, on the other hand, rarely spin fast; the only ones that do so, in fact, are members of twin systems. Moreover, there is no steady gradation of rotational speed from stars like Alnitam to stars like the sun. All the hotter stars tend to spin fast, and there is a sudden break in the average speed of rotation between stars like Sirius and stars like Procyon.

The sun, it will be remembered, is even further down the series than Procyon (Fig. 2). Stars still further down the series — the small red-dwarf stars — spin slowly too. If they did not, the rapid rotation would blur their spectrum lines, but these lines are sharp. We recall the puzzle presented by the solar system: the sun has only a small percentage of the total rotational energy of the whole. Theories of the development of the solar system must imagine a way in which the sun can have unloaded the rotational energy that must have been present in the primeval solar system. The fact that the smaller, cooler stars also spin slowly shows that the problem is not peculiar to the sun; if they started out as brighter, hotter, swiftly rotating stars, they too must have shed their energy of spin. Perhaps the loss of spin energy takes place for all such stars, whether or not they develop with systems of planets.

The Variables in the Great Nebula. — Innumerable stars that fall below the sun in sequence, the stars that make up the bulk of the stellar population, are scattered over the face of Orion. In the very heart of the constellation is a dense group of stars that are almost all as faint as the sun or fainter. They lie within the Great Nebula (Plate 23), and are a great deal more numerous than such stars usually are in a comparable volume. Under careful scrutiny they emerge as something very different from the sun.

The first thing that strikes us is that these stars are all varying in brightness; they flicker and flare in a quite irregular way, very different from the rhythmic fluctuations of the Cepheids and the long-period variables. The spectra of these stars, which have been studied by Greenstein and by Struve, are very peculiar, with the earmarks of glowing gases around them, especially near the fainter ones. Most of them are basically as cool as the sun, or cooler; but the glowing gases suggest far higher temperatures. The hotter stars in the region (which are also the brighter ones), seem to lack these glowing auras. And yet a few of the faint stars, surrounded by glowing clouds, have the colors of hot stars.

Superficially, these variable stars, within the Great Nebula, hardly resemble the sun. But perhaps a sun with a vastly exaggerated chromosphere might resemble the fainter ones; perhaps a sun with a greatly enhanced flare activity might look like the faint anomalous hot ones. The hot, bright stars in the district are probably so hot that their surface radiations actually blow away the enmeshing gases from their surfaces, and therefore they lack t ne glowing auras.

The fact that the peculiar variable stars within the Orion Nebula are perhaps ten times as common as would be expected in an average region suggests that *the presence of the nebula is in some way responsible for their very existence.* Perhaps they are actually being formed within it from the loose dust and gas of which it consists, and the glowing clouds that surround them are the atoms that are condensing to form them. Or possibly they are preëxisting stars that have sailed into this dense region of dust and gas, and are drawing the loose particles into themselves, growing brighter and more massive as they do so. In other words, perhaps in the Orion Nebula we are actually witnessing the birth of stars; or perhaps stars are being rejuvenated before our eyes.

The little group in Orion is not unique. A very similar region, studied by A. H. Joy, lies in the neighboring constellation Taurus; and here there are two or three times as many stars within a dark nebula as are found on the average in an equal volume. Other similar groups have been studied by Struve and his collaborators in the dark clouds of Scorpio and Ophiuchus, in Corona Austrina, and elsewhere, and are very likely to be found in all dense regions of loose dust and gas. The Russian astronomer Ambartsumian surmises that our stellar system contains several thousand of them. Whether they represent the actual birth of stars, or the rapid growth of stars in the presence of abundant nourishment, they show without doubt an important stage in stellar development.

The Variety of Stars. — The constellations of Orion and the Dogs reveal a bewildering variety of stars. We have looked only at their faces, spoken of their size, weight, and temperature. They range from the giant Betelgeuse to the tiny companion of Sirius, from the hot stars of the Trapezium to the cool of the long-period variables.

Great as is the variety of stars, they are to some extent standardized. Most of those that we know run in a continuous series from bright to faint, from hot to cool, from massive to light, from larger to smaller. This series is usually called the *main sequence* (Fig. 2). The brightest main-sequence stars are about ten thousand times as bright as the sun; the faintest, perhaps a millionth as bright. Their sizes range from perhaps twenty times to perhaps one tenth of the sun's, their temperatures from half a million to a couple of thousand degrees, and their weights from forty times to about one tenth the sun's. The great majority of all our neighbors belong to the main sequence: Alnitam and Sirius, Procyon and the sun, and innumerable fainter stars that we have not called by name.

There is another group of stars, somewhat parallel to the main sequence, but (temperature for temperature) fainter, smaller, and probably less massive — the *subdwarfs.* Yet another, the *subgiants,* contains stars, at the same temperatures, rather larger and less dense than those of the main sequence. The *giant stars,* about a hundred times as bright as the sun, are coolish or cool stars like Arcturus and Aldebaran, probably much more massive than the sun, and proportionately less dense. The *supergiants,* like Rigel and Betelgeuse, are still more brilliant. Finally, the *white dwarfs,* the stellar bankrupts, of small size, moderate mass, and extraordinarily high density, form a very numerous group, cut off from the other stars by difference of construction, and — even more significant — of nutrition. All these kinds of stars have parts to play in the drama of the stellar communities that people the cosmic scene. Hitherto we have given portraits of the individuals; in a later chapter we shall consider the situations in which they are found, their relation to one another, and the roles in which they are cast.

The brilliant stars, both hot and cool, are stealing the scene.

28

But they are the exception, negligible in numbers compared with the rank and file. Their brilliance strikes the eye, even from afar, at a distance where a star like the sun would pass unnoticed. If the stars of our neighborhood are herded together for a collective portrait, we realize not only that the fainter ones are far more numerous, but also that they give out the greater part of the light. Stars like Rigel are ten thousand times as bright as the sun. But stars like the sun are at least ten thousand times as numerous as stars like Rigel. Most of the light that fills interstellar space comes from the faint, inconspicuous stars, not from the brilliant ones that dominate the scene. An even greater portion of the mass of all the stars is contained in the faint ones. And, as we shall see in the next chapter, a large fraction of the matter in the cosmos — at least in our part of it — is not part of stars at all, but is spread between them in clouds of dust and atoms.

2   Dust and Atoms

The sun is moving rapidly through space. The stars, greater and lesser suns, have their motions too. We are carried along as passengers in a great stream of stellar traffic. Most of the stars near to us are taking the same road round a great circular track within the Milky Way. The sun moves a little faster round the track than the average stellar traveler, and gains about 12 miles a second on the general stream of traffic. The actual rate of travel is very much larger than this; the average speed in our part of the cosmic highway is about 125 miles a second, over seven thousand times as fast as a car that is going at a mile a minute.

Not all stars keep to the circular track. Our system is, so to speak, full of stellar jaywalkers that are crossing our path at all angles. In fact, in remote parts of our stellar system such stars are more numerous than stars that move in circles, and the two groups differ in character as well as in the paths they travel. The cosmic traffic laws are of great significance in our study of stellar histories, as we shall see later.

At first sight our own part of the cosmic highway seems to be exceptionally crowded. But this is an illusion. Actually we can see only the travelers that are comparatively near to us in our own system of stars; the far side of the track is completely out of sight. And yet other stellar systems, separated from our own Milky Way by vast tracts of empty space, are easily observed at much greater distances than the far side of our own. The reason is that we move in a haze of interstellar dust and smoke, which lies thick in our traffic lane, and thins out rapidly overhead. We can see some of our fellow travelers on the circular track through the fog, but only those that are fairly near to us. Stars that move above or below the track (for cosmic highways have three dimensions) are more easily seen, even at much greater distances.

The system of stars in which our sun moves is but one of billions that are dispersed through space. Its shape is that of a gigantic pancake; or perhaps a very thin layer cake, with a central filling, thick with dust and smoke, within which the circular traffic stream moves. The stars lie thickest near the central plane, and thin out rapidly above and below it. The filling probably does not extend through the center of the cake, but is very likely spilling out at the edges.

The other stellar systems that populate space have various forms. Some are quite devoid of filling; some have much. Through some the central layer is unevenly spread; many are beautifully symmetrical; some are broken and distorted. We shall find that the presence of a central filling is closely related to the shapes of stellar systems and to the nature of the stars that populate them. Interstellar dust and gas are a potent factor in stellar development.

Interstellar Dust. — As we look toward the edges of our flattened stellar system we see the hazy band of light that we call the Milky Way — light from myriads of faint and distant stars that stretch away to the confines of the galaxy (Plates 12 and 13). But the Milky Way is not an unbroken band of brightness. It is crossed by gigantic rifts, fretted with obscuring clouds, wreathed with streaks of dark material, evidences of the dense and patchy interstellar fog that lies between the stars. Nearby patches of dark material are easily seen. The Coal Sack (Plates 13 and 15), under the shoulder of the Southern Cross, is one of the most striking. The whole neighborhood is covered with interstellar fog wreaths. Similar streaks of dark are found everywhere along the Milky Way, where the stellar traffic is heaviest. They cannot be lanes in which there are no stars. When the stellar system was thought to be fairly small, such lanes were a possibility; but now that its great extent is realized, empty lanes are seen to involve immense, straight tunnels devoid of stars, and all pointing directly toward our position — a fantastically improbable

31

arrangement. Today we picture a layer full of patchy haze that extends throughout the Milky Way. The large, nearby pockets of dust can be seen, and so can innumerable knots of dark material that happen to lie in front of a bright surface, such as a nebula close to us (Plate 35). The distant scene must be dimmed by the cumulative effect of such hazy regions, large and small. Without doubt there are many patches so tiny as to be individually invisible, even at close range; indeed, they are probably more numerous than the large ones.

The interstellar dust clouds seemed at first to have only a nuisance value. They interfered with attempts to make a census of the stars, because they compelled us to peer through a dense and patchy fog. To make allowance for the fog in surveying our stellar neighbors is a very difficult task. A star that lies behind a dense cloud is dimmed, and looks farther away than it really is. The cumulative effect of the innumerable small patches of cloud makes the stars seem to thin out rapidly in all directions, especially toward the edges of our flattened system, where the clouds lie thickest. Thus it comes about that our own neighborhood seems exceptionally crowded. Actually the stellar traffic is considerably denser in some other parts of the central layer, but the fact was realized only after a laborious allowance had been made for the distribution of the dust and haze.

At first the interstellar dust was studied with the purpose of removing its effects from our picture of our own system of stars, but before long its own individuality attracted attention. There is a surprising amount of it. The interstellar material in our own district weighs about as much as the stars! Haze and stars form a greater system, and their interplay governs the development of the system. The stars may do the dancing, but, as we shall see, the haze calls the tune.

Stars are known by the light they radiate; but interstellar dust can be studied only by what it conceals. We might well expect that its character would elude analysis; and yet we know a surprising number of things about it: the size of the particles, what they are made of, how they are distributed, even how they are oriented!

When the stars seen through haze were carefully examined, a

striking fact emerged: their light is not only dimmed, but also reddened, like that of the sun as it sets in a murky sky. A star of a given temperature has a given color, and we have already seen that the sun, brightest in yellow light, has a temperature of about 6000°. But there is another way to tell a star's temperature: the atomic lines in its spectrum reveal the conditions at the surface, and from these again the sun's temperature is found to be about 6000°. If we can study a star's spectrum, its temperature can be determined, and in this way we find that stars seen through dark clouds are redder than we should expect from the information given by the atoms in their atmospheres. The colors of stars seen through haze always correspond to a temperature *lower* than would be expected from their spectra. For some stars the difference is amazing: a star that must (from its *spectrum*) have a surface temperature of 30,000° may have the *color* of a star at 4000°.

The piecing together of the information on obscuration and reddening has been the work of many years, and has called for measurements of the greatest precision. Even today it is far from complete. Two results have emerged from it: the amount of reddening is proportional to the amount of absorption; and the relation is the same almost everywhere. The first result provides the most powerful method available for allowing for the dimming of distant stars by interstellar material, and finding their true distances. The second allows us to conclude that the absorption and reddening are nearly everywhere produced by essentially similar processes.

The light of distant stars is reddened by the intervening haze because it is *scattered*, and the bluer the light, the greater is the scattering effect. In other words, the redder the light, the less it is scattered and therefore the more of it can get through the haze. For this reason the sun, as it sets in a hazy atmosphere, seems reddened — the light passes through thicker and thicker layers as the sun sinks toward the horizon.

Yellow light penetrates haze more freely than blue light, red light than yellow light. Light beyond the red limit of eye sensitivity gets through more readily still. So it comes about that distant stars are more easily detected by infrared light than by the blue light of an ordinary photograph. Photographic plates sensitized for the infrared, and instruments for the direct detection of infrared rays, can survey our murky "filling" better than the ordinary plate or the eye. Microwaves (radio waves) come through with even greater ease, and the central regions of our stellar system, completely cut off from ordinary photography, can easily be studied by microwaves — a branch of astronomy that is only now opening up almost unbounded vistas.

An ounce of matter, placed before a star in a solid chunk, would be quite invisible. A similar mass, if pulverized, might absorb a great deal of light. The stopping power depends partly on what the material is made of (whether metallic or nonmetallic) but principally on the sizes of the particles. For example, a mass of material that consists of nonmetallic grains 0.0000014 cm in radius absorbs ten thousand times as much light as the same mass distributed in grains 0.44 cm in radius, and spread over the same area. Nonmetallic grains of 0.0000044-cm radius are four times as efficient still under the same circumstances. If the grains are metallic, the greatest efficiency is about one third that of the nonmetallic grains, and is attained at even smaller size, 0.00000044 cm.* If the subdivision is carried even further, and the mass is resolved into atoms, it becomes almost completely transparent.

The interstellar haze is unlikely to consist of particles of just one size; all sizes must be present, from large chunks down to molecules and atoms. The most efficient ones, however, are the ones that are responsible for the greatest amount of scattering and the absorption; all are acting on the light, but (to use a mixed metaphor) we hear those that shout the loudest.

That the particles are all purely metallic, or purely nonmetallic, is also unlikely. Metals, such as iron, are less common in the stars than hydrogen, carbon, oxygen, nitrogen, and so on; and large proportions of these elements are probable in the interstellar haze. Absorption is related to color of light in a way that suggests that the particles are metallic (though a similar relation would be given by nonmetallic particles of a certain size). Another fact that points to iron (or some other metal with magnetic properties) as a con-

---

* These calculations, made by Greenstein, apply to spherical grains; the grains in interstellar space are not necessarily — in fact probably not — spherical.

stituent of the interstellar grains is the *polarization* * of the scattered light, in a way that shows that the particles are aligned in space. If, as seems most likely, magnetic fields are responsible for the alignment, some at least of the particles must have magnetic properties, and nonmetals are only slightly magnetic. But the interstellar particles reflect light more brilliantly than snow, and only nonmetallic particles could do so. Perhaps the grains are primarily nonmetallic, with small metallic particles embedded in them. The subject is in a state of lively and interesting controversy at the present time.

Atoms in Interstellar Space. — The interstellar material is of many sizes — grains, powder, dust, and particles even smaller. Round the solid matter hovers a haze of molecules, atoms, and electrons. We have seen that atoms and molecules do not block off much light. In fact, a cloud of them between the stars would be almost completely transparent.

Atoms do, however, cut off light in a special way. As we learned in examining the light of the sun, every atom can take up a limited array of colors, sharply bounded and peculiar to that atom. The atoms that lie between the stars are no exception. They rob the starlight of their own particular colors.

We see our own sun through a cloud of atoms — the constituents of the earth's atmosphere — and they leave their mark on sunlight (Plate 18). Molecules of ozone, the triple oxygen molecule, cut off practically all the sun's ultraviolet light by their characteristic absorptions — and it is lucky for us that they do, for the ultraviolet rays of the sun could give us a severe sunburn! The oxygen molecule — two atoms of oxygen knit together by the interlacing of their hazes of electrons — cuts an intricate pattern out of red and infrared sunlight, and so do the molecules of water vapor, carbon dioxide, and other chemical compounds that populate the air. When the sun is overhead, and seen vertically through the atmosphere, the absorptions are weaker than when it lies nearer the horizon and we view it through a thicker layer of air. The more atoms lie in a line between us and the sun, the more deeply is the pattern etched on sunlight.

We see distant stars through clouds of atoms, too — the atoms

* Ordinary light may be pictured as vibrating in all planes in space; polarized light vibrates in a restricted plane.

that are scattered throughout space. Spectrum lines that come from atoms in space can be distinguished from the lines of atoms in the stars' own atmosphere in several ways. They may be narrow, whereas the lines of the star are broad. They always come from atoms in states of low energy, for interstellar material is relatively cool, as compared to the material in stellar envelopes. Most important of all, they can be distinguished by the speed of the atoms that produce them.

Light that comes from atoms that are approaching us is rendered bluer — the light waves are crowded together in space, the wavelength grows smaller, and the light more blue. If the atoms are moving away, the light waves are spaced more widely, the wavelength grows larger, and the light is reddened. The change of color and wavelength of light from a moving source is exactly similar to the change of pitch of a bell or whistle on a moving train: as the train passes the observer the pitch of the sound seems to drop. As the source approaches, the sound waves are crowded together by its motion and the pitch of the note is raised; as it recedes, the sound waves are spread apart and the pitch falls. The effect of the moving source on the color and wavelength of light is known as the spectroscopic Doppler effect. It should not be confused with the quite different reddening effect of the interstellar dust, which reddens by *removing* the blue light from the continuous band of colors given out by the surface of the star. The Doppler effect *changes the wavelengths of absorption lines* in the spectrum, and does not noticeably affect the color of the star as a whole.

The exact wavelength of the light in spectrum lines is measured with a spectroscope. And from the comparison with the wavelengths of lines of the same atom (obtained in the laboratory) that are not moving toward us or away, the speeds of distant atoms, in space or in the stars, can be measured. Suppose we see, from the wavelengths of lines in a star's atmosphere, that it is approaching us at a speed of 50 miles a second; then if one or two lines that cross the spectrum tell of atoms that are *receding* from us at 30 miles a second, we can surmise that the aberrant lines are not part of the light of the star, and can guess (especially if they are low-energy lines) that they come from atoms that are scattered in space between us and the star.

An especially neat proof comes from the pairs of stars that are going round each other in orbits. In the next chapter we shall have much to say about such stars. As they circle round (and if the plane of the orbit lies in the right direction) these stars alternately come toward us and recede from us, and their light is alternately reddened and blued by the Doppler effect (Plate 19). But the light from the interstellar atoms suffers no such periodic change of wavelength, and can be identified with certainty. Calcium, sodium, iron, titanium can actually be seen in the spaces between the stars, and even some simple chemical compounds have been detected. A few of the interstellar lines are still a mystery — we do not know what atoms or molecules produce them.

The interstellar lines tend to cut most strongly into the spectra of very distant stars, especially those that lie in the central dust layer of our stellar system. Their strength, in fact, has been used as a means of guessing stellar distances. But it is an uncertain means of doing so, for the interstellar atoms, like the dust and haze, are distributed in patches.

The spectra of some distant stars show not only one but several representatives of the light absorbed by certain interstellar atoms (such as calcium atoms that have lost one of their electrons). There can be no doubt that all these lines come from similar atoms, and they tell of several groups of atoms that are moving at different rates. Evidently *these stars are seen through several different clouds of atoms*, that are moving with relative speeds of 10 or 20 miles a second, as was shown by Adams. Here we have evidence of large clouds of atoms, that are swirling and churning about in space. The vast regions between the stars are neither empty nor quiescent. They contain moving clouds of atoms, and patches of dust and haze that are probably riding the atomic winds, just as the clouds of our own atmosphere are borne along by invisible air masses.

Bright Nebulae. — The dust, smoke, and interstellar atoms are not analyzed only by their blocking-off power. Some of them can be directly observed in the form of bright *nebulae* (Plates 20 and 23), the gleaming clouds that variegate the Milky Way.

A familiar sight in the winter sky is the constellation Taurus, the Bull that fronts Orion and the Dogs. Everybody knows the Pleiades (Plate 21), the compact cluster of bright stars:

Many a night I saw the Pleiads, rising thro' the mellow shade,
Glitter like a swarm of fire-flies tangled in a silver braid.

The eye sees the fireflies; the photographic plate reveals the silver braid — a gleaming haze that surrounds the bright cluster. The stars are meshed in a network of shining strands, which stretch far from them into the surrounding space.

The shining haze is a cloud of small particles that reflect the light of the Pleiades as brightly as a snowfield. It sends back the pattern of light unchanged — the nebula that surrounds the Pleiades really shines by reflection. Its intricate network of clouds, so fine in detail that it eludes our most powerful telescopes, shows how streaky and patchy is the distribution of interstellar particles. Many of the bright nebulae that adorn the Milky Way are very similar.

But many of the other interstellar clouds do not shine merely by reflection. The Great Nebula of Orion (Plate 23), for instance, swirling around the Trapezium, glows with a light quite different from that of the hot stars within it.

The bright nebulae glow with many colors. Far stronger than the hydrogen glow in the Orion nebula is the light of the so-called "nebular lines," red, green, blue, and ultraviolet. These spectral colors, never produced in the laboratory, were long supposed to emanate from a substance unknown on earth, which received the name "nebulium." Other such hypothetical substances have occurred in the history of astrophysics, but they have not stood the test of time. The first was the source of the yellow light observed in the solar prominences at the eclipse of 1874. Norman Lockyer dubbed it "helium," the sun-element. Today helium is well known on earth, and it is actually the second commonest kind of atom in the cosmos. "Coronium," the supposed source of the bright lines in the sun's corona, is now known to consist of well-known metallic atoms, such as iron, nickel, and calcium. "Nebulium" is of equally prosaic origin: it is of common material, such as oxygen, nitrogen, and neon, but under conditions far from prosaic.

Each atom, as we have seen, possesses its own array of colors, can shine with them, or can rob light of them. An atom that has taken up its own peculiar color is then loaded with energy, which it has a natural tendency to fire off again. A given atom can emit only the colors that make up its natural array (or spectrum); and it gives off some colors far more readily than others. Indeed, we can often calculate the readiness of a given atom to fire off its various possible colors. Some are radiated so readily that the atom waits only a million-millionth of a second before emitting them; for others the interval is longer, and the corresponding color (given out by fewer atoms in a given interval) shines less brightly.

Each atomic species possesses not one, but a vast number of discrete colors. For each atomic species has its own particular complement of electrons, which are distributed in a sort of intricate fog about the nucleus. When an atom radiates light, some of the energy of the electron fog is lost to it, and passes out in a pulse of radiation. When an atom absorbs light, the radiant energy is taken up by the electron fog, and the fog accommodates itself to the acquisition by assuming a new distribution of energy.

The core of our understanding of spectra is the fact that the energies of the circumambient electrons are *quantized* —they can have only discrete values, and they can change only by discrete amounts. The rules that govern the possible changes have fascinating intricacy, and the analysis of all the resulting colors is a crossword puzzle on the cosmic scale.

Thus it comes about that the array of possible colors that an atom can emit depends not only upon how many electrons are present in the fog, but also upon the way their energy is distributed. If the electron fog of an atom is heavily loaded with energy we say that the atom is *excited*; if it has received more energy than it can sustain, and one or more electrons have been detached, and have carried away the excess energy, the atom is said to be *ionized*.

An excited atom will readjust its haze of electrons, and unload its energy, in an array of colors different from those given out by an unexcited atom, and an ionized atom, so far as its spectrum is concerned, is a new kind of atom altogether. So the colors that an atom radiates depend not only on how many electrons the atom possesses, but also on how the energy is distributed among them.

The lines in the spectra of nebulae that were first ascribed to the hypothetical "nebulium" were shown by Bowen, only a couple of decades ago, to originate principally in atoms of oxygen and nitrogen that had lost one or two of their full complement of electrons. The remaining electron haze is only very slightly excited, and is in a so-called "metastable state," that is, a state from which the likelihood of unloading the energy of excitation is very small. None the less, energy is ejected after the appropriate interval, and the nebula shines with the characteristic colors.

How is it that these colors had not been seen on earth, or recorded in the spectra of stars? The answer is that both terrestrial and stellar atoms undergo the same transitions; but only a very tiny fraction of them do so, because the likelihood of the change is extremely small. These spectrum lines have accordingly received the rather unfortunate name of "forbidden" lines. But the transitions are not forbidden, they are only very rare, and it is quite incorrect to suppose that physical processes that are possible in nebulae are not permitted elsewhere. We see the light that comes from "forbidden" lines in nebulae because such an enormous volume of atoms is involved, and even though any one atom performs the change only at long intervals, the cumulative effect of millions of millions of atoms is great enough to be recorded.

The atoms in a bright nebula are thought to be forced into the metastable states by collisions with electrons that are flying through space. The conditions within a bright nebula are almost beyond imagination. Each cubic centimeter contains no more than a thousand atoms — a ten-thousand-millionth of the density in a laboratory discharge tube. Once in every ten years, on the average, an electron is ripped off an atom, and becomes available for exciting another atom to a metastable state. The electrons move among the atoms at perhaps 60 miles a second; they hit an atom once in a decade; once in a million years they may hit a solid grain. Only because of the enormous volume of a nebula are its radiations visible to us. The Orion Nebula is so enormous that we see a million million atoms for every square centimeter of area, and enough of them are executing the rare "forbidden" transitions at any moment to give out appreciable light.

Details of the light even enable us to deduce the density of electrons. When electrons are very sparse, green light will predominate in the nebula; when they are more frequent, blue radiations will be more intense. Almost all nebulae shine most brightly in green light — the Orion Nebula looks slightly green to the eye — and we conclude that the density of electrons is low. But in a few — a very few — the blue radiations predominate, and there the electrons must be denser.

The Orion Nebula and many of the other great nebulae in our system are irregular in form, and close analysis shows that they are bunched and shredded, and resemble clouds of various kinds. Like the dark matter and the reflecting nebulae, the shining atoms are distributed in patchy fashion, torn and swirled by forces not fully understood.

Some of the bright nebulae are much more compact and symmetrical than the one in Orion. Such is the celebrated "Ring Nebula in Lyra" (Plate 24), a star surrounded by a gaseous ring that shines with the characteristic nebular radiations. The "rings" of the so-called planetary nebulae * are observed to be blowing off from the central stars, always found to be at very high temperature; the ring is almost certainly the result of an explosive ejection from the star's surface. Some planetaries have two concentric rings, as though two explosions have taken place, a million or more years apart. Many are unsymmetrical rather than ringlike.

Stellar Explosions. — The explosive ejection of a star's surface can be watched on a grand scale in the outburst of a nova, or "new star." There is nothing new about a nova except the explosion; in fact, "new stars" are probably very old stars that are taking a drastic way out from an intolerable state, when they can no longer support themselves in the style to which they have been accustomed.

Some such stars blow off more or less regularly every few weeks; others, more violent, suffer an upheaval every few years; the bright novae explode infrequently — perhaps every few thousand, or even

---

* They have, of course, nothing to do with planets. They received the name because many show appreciable disks.

41

every million years. The most spectacular of all, the supernovae, seem to blow up once for all, the greatest explosion that man can witness. All of them, in their degree, blow off part of their own substance into space.

The adventures of the stuff that a nova blows off from its surface can be traced in detail from the characteristic radiations. In the first few hours the star simply swells up with great rapidity. Some have blown up at about 2500 miles a second! The surface grows larger and larger, the star becomes brighter and brighter, and it seems as though the skin is stretching and stretching, like that of a balloon. Quite suddenly the brightness reaches its peak, the skin appears to burst, and great surges of glowing material pour out from within. The star behaves like a gigantic Roman candle: glowing globes of gas may shoot out on opposite sides, the surface may vibrate violently, wave after wave surges up to the surface, and atoms spray outward in all directions (Plate 26). This picture is no flight of the imagination; every detail can be pieced together from a study of the spectrum.

At first the ejected material shows evidence of fairly high density: after the surface bursts, the light of glowing atoms, a gigantic chromosphere, is seen against the body of the star. But soon a change takes place: the chromosphere continues to expand at fantastic speed; the atoms thin out, the density falls, and the "forbidden" lines appear. First come those that go with high density of electrons; the envelope glows like an aurora. Then, as the gases grow more tenuous, the expanding mass glows like a nebula. At last the spray of atoms ceases, the gases thin out into space, the bright radiations die away, and the nova fades to its former brightness. Novae are spectacular, but with most of them it is "all cry and little wool" — the mass that is blown off in the explosion is a tiny fraction of the whole, and the cataclysm, whatever its cause, leaves the star essentially unchanged. Only for the supernovae is the cataclysm really a catastrophe: the greater part of the star is blown off into space, only a fragment is left behind — a tiny star in place of the giant that was rent asunder.

The interesting thing about an exploding nova, from our present standpoint, is that after it has expanded far enough, its spectrum is very like that of a planetary nebula, just as the spectrum of a planetary nebula is very like that of the Nebula in Orion. In a nova we actually witness a star in explosion; in a planetary nebula we believe that the glowing envelope is the relic of such an explosion. But (unless we are greatly mistaken) the gases that glow in the Orion Nebula were never part of a star. All the matter spewed out by novae, by planetary nebulae, or by the stars (mentioned in the last chapter) that are gradually losing their chromospheres would not add up to as much loose material as we can observe lying thick in the stellar traffic ways. Nebulae like the one in Orion must represent the primitive prestellar material. It is a most important discovery that matter that has "gone through the mill" as part of a star has just the same properties *and composition* as matter that has never been stellar.

The conclusion can even be made quantitative. By a knowledge of the relative tendencies of atoms to absorb and emit their different characteristic colors, the atoms in stellar envelopes, exploding novae, and planetary nebulae can actually be counted. The diffuse nebulae are harder to treat, but the general result is the same. The verdict seems to be "no difference," either in the kinds or the relative numbers of atoms present. The interstellar gas offers a typical sample of the atomic composition of the fundamental material out of which the stars were built.

The supernovae tell a different story (Plate 27). Their spectra are an enigma, different from those of anything else ever observed. But though it is hard to say what they are made of, we can assert with some confidence what they are *not* made of: they seem to contain very little hydrogen, the substance par excellence of which nearly all stars, and all galactic nebulae, are made. We have learned that stars subsist on hydrogen; what could be more suggestive than the observation that the supernovae, the only stars that are observed to undergo *radical* change under our eyes, seem to be short of this commodity? It is not too fantastic to regard them as stellar bankrupts in liquidation.

The expanding envelopes of novae, the planetary nebulae, the bright nebulae of the galaxy, do not exhaust our knowledge of interstellar nebulosity. The whole of our part of the galaxy is pervaded

43

by a tenuous haze of glowing atoms. They are too far apart, too diffuse, to appear as individual bright nebulae, but their light can be photographed with specially designed equipment. The scattered gas is incredibly diffuse — about one atom per cubic centimeter, less than one thousandth of the density of the Orion Nebula. Sparse as it is, this interstellar gas is spread through such an enormous volume that its *average* density is not far from that of all stars in the same region. There is about as much nonstellar as stellar material in our district, the central traffic lane of the stellar system. A little of this interstellar material may have been ejected by stars, but most of it is probably primitive; it has never been stellar in the past. Its effect on stars, and its own probable future, are major themes in the drama of evolution.

Atoms in the Cosmos. — In the first chapter we examined the many-sided character of the sun — its capacity for producing an enormous range of spectra under a huge variety of conditions. We reflected on the possibility that the other stars may display a different interplay of the same conditions.

The present chapter has surveyed the many-sided character of the atoms. The same atoms can be responsible, in different conditions, for a vast range of appearances. Oxygen, for example, runs the gamut of its possible behavior between earth and nebula. In our own air we find the oxygen molecule, two atoms bound together by electron interaction. The twin oxygen molecule cuts an intricate pattern out of the spectrum of sunlight. Thirty miles up in the atmosphere, the ozone molecule (three oxygen atoms bound together) obscures the ultraviolet light of the sun. Still higher in the atmosphere the single atom of oxygen, complete with its full complement of eight electrons, is excited to "forbidden" transitions at low density, and gives characteristic color to the aurora. Far away, in the atmosphere of the sun and stars, we see the normal colors typical of various oxygen atoms (some with one or more electrons stripped away) cut out from the starlight. And in the almost complete vacuum of interstellar space we trace the "forbidden" lines of atoms of oxygen that have lost one or two of their outermost electrons.

Hydrogen, too, runs the gamut of cosmic conditions. Sunlight is scored by the spectrum lines of water vapor — hydrogen and oxygen combined. Lines of hydrogen in our own atmosphere tell of hydrogen atoms showering on us from the sun. Hydrogen cuts out characteristic colors from the spectra of sun and stars. Hydrogen is responsible, too, for the lack of transparency of the lower layers of stellar atmospheres. We see the glowing atoms of hydrogen in the bright nebulae, such as that in Orion, and the fainter light of the hydrogen atoms that extend in a diffuse haze throughout the central layer of the stellar system. The interstellar hydrogen even appears in the radio waves that are given out from its thinly scattered atoms when the electrons that accompany them suddenly change their orientation.

And we have not exhausted the roles played by the hydrogen atom in the cosmos. All the behavior just enumerated is very superficial — the work of the electron that accompanies the hydrogen nucleus. We must look beneath the electronic trappings for the heart of the drama. The nucleus of a hydrogen atom — the particle that is well named the *proton* — is the core of stellar life. We cannot observe it directly, but by its effects we see the universe of stars.

PART TWO

THE SCENE

3 Pairs of Stars

The stream of traffic races around its immense track within the stellar system. As we peer through the haze at the nearer travelers we notice a remarkable thing. Few stars are making the journey alone. They travel in pairs, often in even larger groups. The greater and lesser Dog Stars, each accompanied by a tiny "pup," are not the exception, but the rule.

Even though pairs of stars are seen only from a distance, they reveal a great deal: each one is a "still picture" of an intimate stellar situation. In the first place, they cannot be fortuitous; when we see two stars moving very close together we are not witnessing a cosmic traffic accident. Large as the stars are, the traffic lane is so broad that the risk of collisions is actually nil; cosmic travel is almost completely safe.

Perhaps it may seem contradictory to say in one breath that stars travel in close pairs and that the traffic is spaced so widely that collisions are impossible. A careful look at the members of a pair dispels the contradiction. There is an intimate relation, a close bond, between them. They are waltzing round the track under strict rules — held together by powerful attraction, but kept apart by the rapid turns of the dance. In more technical terms, they describe orbits round each other under their mutual gravitational attraction.

The orbital motion of pairs of stars was discovered by accident. Late in the eighteenth century, William Herschel looked for a way of detecting the *parallax* of the stars — the periodic shift of nearby objects against the distant stellar landscape as the earth makes the yearly circuit of its orbit. He chose a number of pairs of stars close together in the sky, in the belief that one of the pair would prove to be more distant than the other. He hoped that the nearer star would seem to shift back and forth against the far-off one at six-month intervals, when it was seen from opposite sides of the earth's orbit. Observation falsified Herschel's expectations. He did not find a back-and-forth shift every six months. He saw instead that the members of his chosen pairs were moving *round each other*, and that they took much more than six months to make the circuit. He snatched victory from defeat, for he realized that he had discovered two tremendous facts: *the pairs of stars are true pairs*, close together in space; and *they move in orbits round each other* under the pull of gravitation. Until that time, the operations of gravitation had been recognized only within the planetary system; Herschel's discovery showed that they also govern the system of the stars.

Herschel realized at once the great significance of these *double stars*, and began to make a list of them. The list has grown so rapidly that, in less than two centuries, tens of thousands of stellar pairs have been discovered. Today we suspect that the great majority of the stars that follow the circular traffic lane are double.

Close together as the members of a double star may be (and some pairs are practically touching), they are safe from collision with each other. Their orbital motion keeps them apart, just as the orbital motion of the planets keeps them from falling into the sun, and the path swept out by the moon prevents it from falling onto the earth. And the stellar traffic is so widely spaced that individual pairs are as unlikely to collide with each other as two couples, one waltzing in New York, the other in California.

From the enormous distances between stellar pairs we can conclude that *stellar unions are practically indissoluble*. Only the attraction of other stars can draw a pair apart. In the thinly spaced traffic of our part of the stellar system, an approach of a star close enough to separate the partners is practically out of the question; more distant encounters have a very slight effect. As time goes on, the influence of innumerable remote stars seems to relax the closeness of the embrace; the members of the pair continue to waltz, but with time they draw a little further apart.

If this conclusion is correct, another follows. *The couples have been even closer in the past.* We can say even more: in the widely scattered traffic stream they can scarcely have come together by accident; *they have been together from the first.*

Here is the enormous significance of double stars: they are pairs that have always been pairs. They were born together as a result of one process; they are of the same age; they have gone through the same experiences. The series of "still pictures" of stellar pairs tells not only of a current situation, a momentary intimate association; it shows the development of two characters that started from the same environment, have passed through similar external circumstances. They are twins that have been brought up together.

Speculation without the facts might lead us to suspect that such twins would always be identical — that stars born together, associated from the beginning, must always remain similar. But the facts are otherwise. Some identical twins there are, but they are the minority; in spite of similar origin and history, many pairs of stars are extraordinarily unlike. Here is one of the cornerstones of our study of stellar evolution: we must explain how a pair of twins can have developed such different characters. Let us look at a few intimate stellar situations, and form a picture of the variety of stellar matings, the closeness of the embrace, the pace of the dance.

Herschel saw pairs that move round each other in orbits. Some move in ellipses, some in circles. For those double stars whose motions can be seen, elliptical orbits (some very much elongated) are the rule, circular orbits the exception. Consider for a moment the necessary conditions for discovering such pairs. The two stars must appear far enough apart to be seen separately. If their distance from each other is extremely great, their gravitational attraction on each other (which, as Newton showed, falls off as the square of the distance between them) will be too small to constrain them to move round each other. The nearest star to the sun is the faint companion of Alpha Centauri, four light-years away. At so great a distance apart, the general influence of all the stars would outweigh the mutual attraction of two stars; the stars of such a pair would affect each other slightly, but they would not describe the closed orbit of a double star. Therefore a pair of stars that are moving round each other must be fairly close together, as compared with the average spacing in the traffic stream. And if we are to see such a pair, it must also be fairly close to us. We can expect to see double stars only among our moderately near neighbors.

Furthermore, a double star is difficult to recognize if the two members differ very much in brightness. Pairs that are nearly of the same brightness are easiest to find, and pairs that differ enormously become progressively more difficult, if only because the fainter member may be very faint indeed, too faint to be seen.

It may happen that the orbital motion of a double star is detected even though only one of the pair is bright enough to see. This actually occurred in the case of Sirius. The Dog Star happens to be one of the nearest stars. It and the sun are moving with the great stream of stellar traffic, but at slightly different speeds; as it overtakes us we see its position shift steadily against the background of the more distant stars; the effect is large because we are not very far apart. In fact, Sirius is so close to us that its path, against the stellar background, can be mapped very accurately indeed. Even a hundred years ago the Dog Star was seen to be traveling, not in a straight line, but in a path that looked wavy. Actually the path is a corkscrew motion seen in projection.

All our knowledge of the motions of heavenly bodies assures us that their paths must be straight lines unless something is disturbing them. The regular corkscrew motion pointed inevitably to some regular disturbance, and orbital motion round some invisible companion exactly filled the bill. One turn of the screw took almost exactly fifty years; the two stars — bright Sirius and its invisible mate — were therefore making one circuit in fifty years. The absolute correctness of this interpretation was demonstrated in 1862, when the companion, the famous "Pup," was actually seen for the first time by Alvan Clark. The pair has been watched since then through almost two complete circuits, and observations show conclusively that the corkscrew path is a combination of orbital motion and motion through space. The "Pup" moves in a corkscrew too, twice as wide as that described by Sirius. In other words, the companion has an orbit twice as large as that of the Dog Star round a mutual center, which moves through space in a straight line.

This brings us to another fact that makes double stars of great significance in the study of the properties of stars in general. *They are the only stars that can be weighed.* When we weigh something in everyday life, we commonly balance it against something else whose weight we know. It is the same in dealing with stars. They can be weighed by balancing them against other stars. The orbits of a pair of stars supply the equivalent of a balance, and the center of gravity of the system corresponds to the fulcrum. The laws of motion, worked out and verified within the planetary system, show that the relative sizes of orbits about the center of gravity are determined by the masses of the components. *The larger the mass, the smaller the orbit.* As the orbit of the "Pup" is nearly twice the size of the orbit of Sirius, the mass of Sirius is nearly twice the mass of the "Pup."

This does not tell us the masses themselves, but only the ratio of the masses to one another. The actual sizes of the two orbits, and the time taken to execute them, are needed if we are to determine the whole mass of the system, Sirius and the "Pup" together — again from the laws of motion that have been verified within the planetary system. And when we know the sum of the masses, the individual masses follow from a very simple calculation.

I have mentioned these rather technical details because I want to explain how stars can actually be weighed, and to make the point that *the only stars that can be weighed are double stars.* The matter is worth stressing, because probably the mass of a star is its most important property. In the first chapter I mentioned that the total output of stellar energy, luminosity, seems to depend almost exclusively on the star's weight (the "mass-luminosity law"). It is important to remember that this conclusion is backed up by evidence only from stars that can be, and have been, weighed — the double stars. We have no method whatever for weighing stars that are traveling alone.

Sirius is about a hundred times as bright as the sun, and the "Pup," less than one hundredth as bright as the sun. In other words, Sirius is over ten thousand times as bright as its companion. But it weighs only twice as much. The "Pup" is one of the most flagrant exceptions to the rule that the mass of a star determines its energy output, the "mass-luminosity law." If it complied with the rule, it would be about as bright as the sun, over a hundred times as bright as it actually is.

The system of Sirius represents a pair of stellar twins (Fig. 1), stars that (so we must believe) originated together and have spent their lives in company. Let us compare them. Sirius is a little hotter

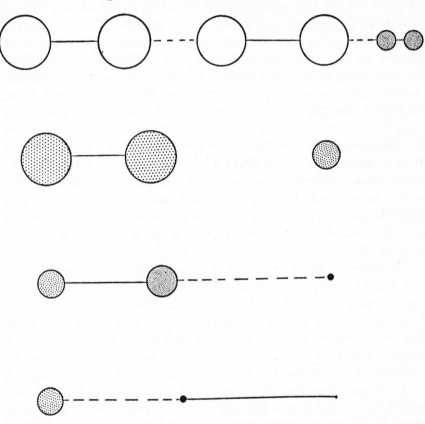

FIG. 3. *Components of four double or multiple stars, drawn to scale, with the sun for comparison. Close pairs are joined by solid lines; wide companions, by broken lines. Top row: the components of Castor. Second row: left, Gamma Virginis; right, the sun. Third row: the components of Alpha Centauri. Fourth row: the components of o² Eridani.*

at the surface, about twice as massive, about sixty times as large, about ten thousand times as bright. The companion has about sixty thousand times the density of Sirius. Anything less like a pair of identical twins can hardly be imagined. Even in their internal economy they differ radically. Sirius is consuming its internal hydrogen steadily by means of the "carbon cycle"; the companion is a stellar bankrupt, incapable of releasing nuclear energy in its interior, probably sustained by gravitational contraction that is slowly converting energy of position into light. The Sirius system displays a remarkable contrast in character development, a contrast that tells of conflicting forces that underlie the drama of stellar evolution.

All stellar twins, however, are not dissimilar. One of the bright naked-eye stars in Virgo is revealed with even a small telescope to consist of two stars, equal in brightness and similar in color. They lie between the sun and Sirius in size, brightness, and mass; and they seem as like as peas. They are going round each other, once in about 200 years, in a very elongated orbit.

Another naked-eye star, Epsilon in the constellation Lyra, can just be detected as a double by the unaided eye: two points of light, the same in brightness and color. They are very far apart, and probably spend hundreds of thousands of years in one circuit of each other. In fact, each of them is itself a twin system, two similar stars that circulate round each other once in several centuries. All four are alike: a little smaller, cooler, and fainter than Sirius — identical quadruplets.

An even more fascinating group is Castor, the brighter of the "Heavenly Twins" in the constellation Gemini. With the telescope, Castor is seen to be triple, but the three stars are not identical; two resemble Sirius in brightness and color, and the third is very faint, very red, far cooler than the sun. Analysis of the spectra reveals that each of the three is a pair of identical twins. Here we have stellar sextuplets: four are stars very like Sirius, and two others are smaller, fainter, lighter, cooler than the sun. The faint red twins go round each other in about 19 hours; one of the pairs of bright twins circulates in three days, and the other in nine. In addition, the two bright pairs swing round each other in about 300 years; the faint red twins circle the system of bright quadruplets in perhaps millions of years. The six stars form a true physical system, bound together by, and intricately moving under, their mutual attractions. They are of the same age and origin, and have shared the same history, but their characters have developed differently.

The nearest of all stars to the sun consists of triplets. It lies in the Southern Hemisphere, in the constellation of the Centaur, and we know it as Alpha Centauri — oddly enough, though it is a bright naked-eye star, it has no familiar name. The triplets are not identical. The brightest is very nearly the sun's twin, in size, brightness, temperature, and mass. The second is a little larger,* but fainter, cooler, and less massive. The third is one of the smallest, coolest stars known, only 6 percent the size of the sun. It lies on the tail end of the main sequence, and is not a white dwarf, although it is a good deal fainter than the companion of Sirius. The two bright stars in the group that makes up Alpha Centauri circulate round their orbit in about 80 years. The tiny companion (known as "Proxima," the nearest, because it is our closest stellar neighbor) has an orbit that is so large that we do not know its time of revolution, and therefore we have not been able to weigh it. But we are certain that it really belongs to Alpha Centauri, because the three are moving through space together at precisely the same rate.

Another well-known set of stellar triplets, the system of o² Eridani, has something in common with Alpha Centauri, but is amazingly different too. The brightest is rather like the sun — a little smaller, cooler, and fainter. The second is rather like Proxima — a very cool main-sequence star, one fifth as massive as the sun, and about one fifth the size. The third star of the group is the surprise — it is a white dwarf, about half as massive as the sun, yet only 2 percent of the sun's size, hence 64,000 times as dense! The red main-sequence star and the white dwarf circulate round each other in about 250 years, and the pair moves about the brightest triplet in a very large orbit.

The double stars that can be watched as they go round each other (visual binaries) make their circuit slowly. Comparatively few have been observed while they made even one complete turn. Visual pairs that circulate in less than a decade are rare; the vast majority require hundreds or even thousands of years. This is partly an accident of discovery: only if the stars take a long time to a circuit — if, as we say, their *periods* are long — are their orbits large; and, as we

---

* In other words, it lies a little above the main sequence; it is a *subgiant* rather than a main-sequence star.

have seen, we shall not see them as individuals unless their orbits *are* large. But there is one trend shown by these "visual double stars" that cannot be fortuitous: most of them travel in elongated orbits rather than circles; and the longer the period, the more elongated the orbit.

A survey of the partnerships revealed by visual double stars exposes considerable variety: we have seen identical twins, from stars resembling Sirius down to faint, small, cool stars. All these identical twins fall near the main sequence described in the first chapter. We have seen dissimilar stars, such as the components of Alpha Centauri and Castor, which differ enormously among themselves, but all lie near the main sequence. And finally, in Sirius, Procyon, and o² Eridani we have met with main-sequence stars in company with white dwarfs, which differ from them fundamentally as well as superficially. A great many white dwarfs are members of twin systems, but some seem to be traveling alone.

None of the visual doubles that we have mentioned has been brighter or hotter than Sirius; although such stars are very rare in space they are bright and conspicuous, and their absence from our list of double stars calls for comment. It would be erroneous to conclude that the very bright, massive, hot stars do not form double systems. In point of fact, there is a greater proportion of doubles among these luminous stars than are to be found further down the main sequence. Why then do we not see motion in their orbits? There are two main reasons. These hot, luminous twins are rare in space, and even the nearest of them is farther away than most of those that we have been discussing. Also, the members of hot, bright pairs are always closer together than the components of visual doubles, so their periods, instead of being reckoned in decades, are only to be counted in days, or even hours; in consequence their orbits are far smaller. Such double systems must be detected by quite different methods.

Close binary systems are found and measured by means of the spectroscope, which (by evaluating the change in color of light that comes from objects approaching or receding from us) can give a direct measure of the speed of a star in our direction. If we know the speed of a star in its orbit, and the time taken to describe the orbit, it is an easy matter to calculate the size of the orbit. In this way the orbit of a star can be mapped out just as certainly as if we were able to see the motion in space. The size of the orbit makes no difference; in fact, for stars of a given mass, the smaller the orbit the faster is the

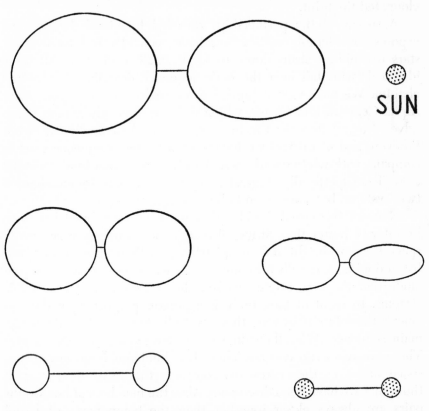

SUN

FIG. 4. *Relative sizes and separations of a number of high-luminosity twin stars, with the sun for comparison. The one on the upper left is UW Canis Majoris. Notice that the close pairs are tidally distorted by their proximity and rapid rotation, but the distant pairs are not.*

motion, and the easier is the double star to detect. Double stars found in this way from the (Doppler) velocity effect on their light are called *spectroscopic binaries*. Many hundreds are known; they are closer together, and their orbits more nearly circular, than for visual binaries.

One property of the orbit is important — the degree to which it is tilted toward the observer. An orbit that is presented exactly

58

face-on will give no observable to-and-fro motion, so a binary that faces its orbit in our direction cannot be detected. If the orbit is more nearly edge-on, it can be detected, but (regrettably) we cannot tell exactly how much it is tipped, so that its size eludes us. If, however, the orbit is presented exactly edge-on, *the two stars will pass one in front of the other regularly in every circuit*, and produce an *eclipse*. If we see an eclipse (or periodic fadeout) for a star that is also a spectroscopic binary, we have everything: the size of the orbit, its tilt, the sizes and masses of the two stars, are all determined.

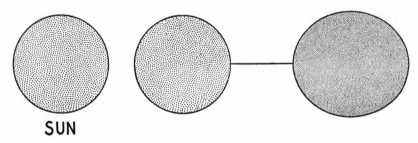

SUN

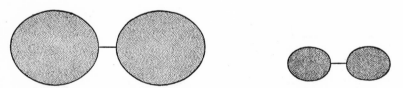

Fig. 5. *Relative sizes and separations of several twin systems as faint as, or fainter than, the sun. (Based on a study by S. Gaposchkin.)*

The calculations, it is true, are most complicated, but in principle the problem can be solved. And the spectroscopic binaries that are also eclipsing stars are the cornerstone of all our knowledge of stellar dimensions. Thousands of eclipsing stars are known — stars that are going round in orbits that are presented to us exactly, or almost exactly, edge-on.

The great majority of the hotter, brighter stars are spectroscopic binaries; in other words, most of the stars at the top of the main sequence are double. There is another feature that is shared by most of the hot, bright stars: they tend to be spinning rapidly. As we approach the cooler, fainter stars, the proportion of binaries falls off, and so does the average speed of spinning. Spinning and twinning, as I said in the first chapter, tend to go together. And the hot, main-

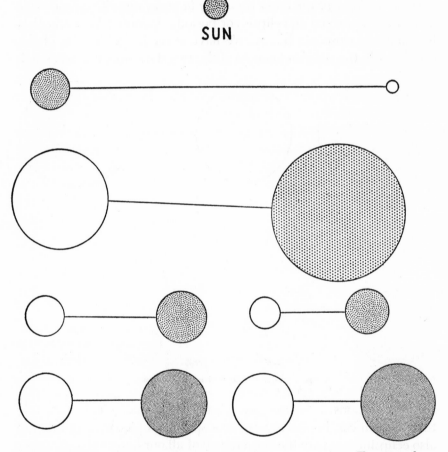

SUN

FIG. 6. *A group of dissimilar pairs of stars, with the sun for comparison. The system shown in the lower left in Algol. (Based on a study by S. Gaposchkin.)*

sequence stars, when they form twins, nearly always form identical twins. When we examine the bright end of the main sequence for dissimilar twins, almost the highest star we find, a little above Sirius, is the "Demon Star," Algol.

The second brightest star in the constellation Perseus, Algol perhaps got its name from the fact that it gives a ghostly wink at intervals of rather less than three days. More careful study shows that it gives another, far less conspicuous, wink halfway between the main ones. To put the matter in more technical form: two stars are moving round each other with a period just under three days, and in a circular orbit that is presented to us almost edge-on. As one star passes between us and the other, it cuts off some light, and an *eclipse* takes place. One of the two stars is much fainter than the other, and when that one is in front, much light is cut off and a conspicuous eclipse occurs; when the brighter star is in front, less light is lost and a less marked eclipse is observed.

The brighter member of the eclipsing pair is a main-sequence star, a little brighter, hotter, and more massive than Sirius. The fainter one is a star of a kind that we have not met before; it is a little larger than its companion, but only one thirteenth as bright, of about one quarter the density, and considerably cooler at the surface. It is too faint to be a giant star, too bright to be on the main sequence; it is a typical specimen of that interesting group of stars known as *subgiants*.

Algol has some peculiarities all its own (for instance, it is a triple system, with one hitherto unseen component, possibly more), but the possession of a subgiant eclipsing companion makes it typical of a large group of double stars. An immense number of "Algol stars" are known, and all of them consist of a brighter main-sequence star (not very far from Sirius in dimensions) and a fainter, less dense, cooler subgiant star. There was a time when all the known subgiants were members of eclipsing pairs, but today we recognize that subgiants can exist independently as well.

Somewhere among stars similar to Sirius we find a division of the double stars with a main-sequence component (discovered as eclipsing stars and spectroscopic binaries) into two groups. One group contains the identical twins; the other consists of dissimilar twins, one of them a subgiant. The identical twins are found as eclipsing pairs, all the way down the main sequence. There are uncommon pairs that look like twins of our sun, spherical and slowly rotating. There are far commoner pairs, the same size, but

61

much closer together, that are spinning rapidly, distorted out of the spherical shape by their speed of rotation. The third pair of twins in Castor is an eclipsing system of slow rotation, far down the main

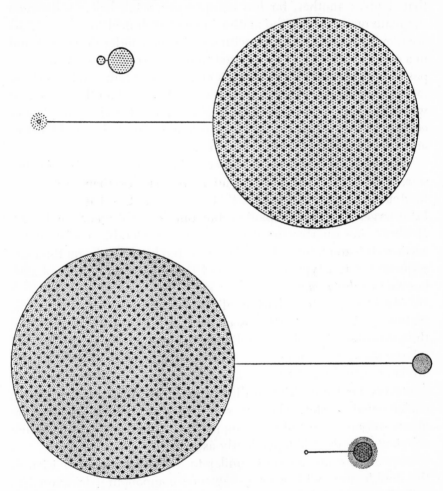

Fig. 7. *Four giant pairs of stars; the sun is so small in comparison that it cannot be shown in the figure. The four pairs are, respectively: W Crucis, VV Cephei, Epsilon Aurigae, and Zeta Aurigae. The two last may be seen on the picture of the constellation Auriga, Plate 30. (Based on a study by S. Gaposchkin.)*

sequence. Other stars of the same size are close together, almost touching, and rotate and revolve with immense speed. Identical twins span the entire main sequence. Most of them are close together, many almost in contact, and almost all have perfectly circular orbits.

The dissimilar twins set in for stars a little brighter than Sirius, and run down the main sequence from there. How far down it they extend is difficult to tell. When one component of a pair is a small, faint dwarf, the pair will manifestly be difficult to detect, for the eclipses will be very short and very shallow.

The most spectacular of all double stars have yet to be mentioned. These are the giant eclipsing systems — pairs that contain huge, distended stars that resemble Canopus, Betelgeuse, and Antares. Among the visual doubles we did not mention any giant stars, though Capella almost qualifies as a visual binary. But in order to see Capella as a binary we have to equip ourselves with artificial eyes many feet apart (the optical device known as the interferometer). Capella turns out to be a pair of twin giants, rather similar in size, brightness, weight, and color. They take about three months to go round each other. Stars like the components of Capella are very rare indeed; in fact, Capella is in some ways unique, with no known counterpart among the stars.

The constellation of Auriga, the Charioteer (Plate 30), contains other remarkable stars than Capella. When you glance at it you look at some of the most stupendous of known stellar twins. The system Zeta Aurigae is an amazing dissimilar pair of stars. These two stars are about equally bright. One is a very hot blue star, a hundred times as bright as the sun, nine times as massive, three and a half times the size. The other is an enormous, cool star, a *supergiant*. It weighs about sixteen times as much as the sun, but is about 245 times the size — larger than the earth's orbit. By a lucky accident, the orbit of Zeta Aurigae is presented to us almost on edge, and we observe an eclipse as the large, cool star passes in front of its neighbor. They take about three years to go round each other. As the eclipse approaches, the blue star is slightly dimmed, *even before the red star comes in front of it*. Evidently the large star has an enormous atmosphere, at least twice its own size. We can picture a huge network of prominences that hover above the surface, dense enough to cut off the light of the companion before the edge of the larger star reaches it. As the envelope of the cool star sweeps into line with

63

the bright star in the rear, it cuts an intricate pattern across the spectrum of its companion, just as the earth's atmosphere cuts a pattern in the sunlight that passes through it.

An even more stupendous system is that of the neighboring star Epsilon Aurigae. Here are two stars that make a turn round each other every 27 years. The brighter star is like the sun in color and temperature, but about 200 times as large — one of the largest and most luminous supergiants. The detail of its spectrum tells of an atmosphere of extreme tenuity. But the companion, which eclipses the brighter star at regular intervals of 27 years, is unlike any other star known. It is so cool that we have never actually seen it, and yet we can tell what it is like by the eclipse that it performs. It has over two thousand times the sun's diameter, less than one millionth of the sun's density!

Our survey of double stars has revealed the extraordinary disparity of stellar matings. All down the main sequence we find identical twins, from the hot, luminous stars that weigh thirty or forty times as much as the sun, down to tiny, cool stars, perhaps a fifth of the sun's weight. Most of these identical twins (though not quite all) are revolving very close together, almost in contact with each other, so that their forms are distorted out of the spherical by tidal attraction. There are a few — a very few — identical twins among the giant and supergiant stars; there is something odd about all of these; they have few counterparts, if any, among single stars. But we have also seen main-sequence stars that are mated with very different stars: unions of stars from very different parts of the sequence; bodies like Algol with a cool, diffuse companion that is a subgiant; systems like that of Sirius that contain a main-sequence star and a white dwarf; systems like Zeta Aurigae that consist of a bright main-sequence star and a diffuse supergiant.

We have seen white dwarfs united with main-sequence stars, most often faint, red ones, more rarely bluer stars like Procyon and Sirius. A few cases are known of white dwarf mated with white dwarf; and such unions may really be quite common, though they are difficult to observe. The unions between giant stars show even greater variety, and even less constant pattern — witness Capella, W Crucis, and Epsilon Aurigae.

If, as we believe, the members of twin systems were born together and have spent their lives in company, the complex of strange
bedfellows, where almost any type of union seems possible, poses a
real problem. The development of stellar character cannot depend
on age alone, or history alone; for pairs of similar age and similar
history have ended up in almost infinite variety.

Each of our series of intimate stellar scenes shows the present
character and current relationship of a pair of twins. It tells little of
the differences in history between different pairs. Something we can
say: the give-and-take of the pull of remote stars gradually relaxes
the closeness of the pair, and also, it seems, renders circular orbits
elliptical. So we can see in the eclipsing and spectroscopic binaries,
revolving close together in orbits nearly circular, pairs with a shorter
history than the widely spaced visual double stars. Happily for us,
the differences can be studied also on a broader scale. In the next
chapter we shall pass from the stellar twins to the great families of
stars, which are associated as closely as the pairs. The common traits
of stellar families throw a flood of light on the scattered situations
that the double stars have revealed.

4   Clusters of Stars

The constellation Taurus, the Bull, glitters in the winter sky (Plate 31). His name comes down from the dawn of history, for he is one of the creatures that mark the path of the sun among the stars — the Zodiac, the Circle of the Beasts. The Babylonians called him the "Bull-in-Front," whose encounter with the sun ushered in the spring. That fact serves to date him: today the sun passes through Pisces, the Fishes, at the vernal equinox, and the change speaks of the slow swinging of the axis of the earth, the precession of the equinoxes that changes the pole star from age to age. When Taurus was named, the pole star was not our familiar Polaris, but the star Alpha Draconis.

To the modern astronomer, Taurus has another interest than as part of the background for the annual motion of the sun. It contains groups of stars with individualities of their own, some of the most significant in the heavens. Taurus lies athwart the Milky Way, where the stellar traffic lies thickest, and here we shall find significant groups of travelers.

The Pleiades. — Everyone knows the Pleiades, the cluster of naked-eye stars that gleam in Taurus "like a swarm of golden bees" (Plate 21). A keen eye can see six (and early legend tells of seven, one of whom was lost as these daughters of Atlas fled from Orion, and were changed into a flock of celestial doves). The telescope reveals several hundred stars in a loose cluster, with the bright, naked-eye members bunched at the center.

The little knot of stars is no accident. They are all at the same distance from us, and careful measures show that they are all moving together through space — a party of stars traveling in company around the great galactic track.

If a pair of stellar twins has not come together by chance, but has always been a pair, how much more certainly must the Pleiades always have been traveling in company! The probability that they happen by accident to be clustered and to be moving along together is nil. Their clustering and their common motion alone are enough to assure us of their common origin.

A mere look at the Pleiades shows us that they differ very much in brightness. The brightest of them is a hundred thousand times as bright as the faintest that has been observed. If we could bring all the members of the cluster to the same distance as the sun, the brightest stars in it would be a thousand times as bright as the sun, the faintest would have but one hundredth of the sun's brightness.

In imagination, the astronomer does that very thing. He lines up the stars of the cluster for a sort of family portrait. By careful measurement of brightness and color * he is able to find the temperatures, and calculate the sizes, of every member of the cluster.

The family portrait of the Pleiades embraces a large variety, not only of brightness, but of temperature and size as well. It is a variety coupled with regularity. The Pleiades form a beautifully graded series of stars. The brightest are also the largest and the hottest (bluest), and the rest run downward, from bright to faint, from large to small, from hot to cool. The middle stars of the sequence are very like the sun in size, brightness, and color. The largest are about nine times the sun's size, perhaps five times its temperature at the surface; the smallest observed are about half the sun's size, rather more than half its temperature. We cannot speak about the actual smallest and faintest, because probably there may be many too faint for us to observe.

The family portrait of the Pleiades, indeed, follows rather closely the backbone of the main sequence that we have already met. We could pick pairs of stars from the group that are related just as the components of Gamma Virginis, or of Castor, are related. The

---

* These measurements are made by means of the accurate light-measuring device, the photoelectric photometer.

Pleiades show, on a far grander scale than any individual pair of double stars, the range of stellar character that can develop from a single beginning.

The Pleiades are close enough to us to reveal many fascinating details. Most of the brighter ones are spinning rapidly, and we know from their spectra that they are spraying atoms into the space around them as they spin. One of them is especially interesting: Pleione has blown several great chromospheric bubbles into space during the past fifty years, and probably has a long history of such events. Perhaps it was brighter in the remote past, and gave birth to the legend of the "Lost Pleiad"; even today it fluctuates slightly in brilliance.

The cluster is meshed in interstellar clouds, which scatter its light. The clouds are not uniform; among the stars they run in great streaks and striations, of such fine detail that no telescope has yet analyzed them down to the finest shred. Perhaps the whirling stars have spun some of this material out into space; it does not consist principally of atoms, but is in the form of solid chunks, which scatter light as brilliantly as snow, and probably the main part of it has always been floating between the stars.

The Pleiades are the brightest and nearest of such clusters, but they are not unique. Dozens of similar groups sprinkle the Milky Way, such as the beautiful little Kappa Crucis, which lies beside the Southern Cross near the Coal Sack and is known to southern observers as "The Jewel Box" (Plate 34). Probably our stellar system contains many hundreds. They are all groups traveling the stellar traffic lane; they have similar family portraits, and perhaps most of them are meshed in nebulosity. Because they populate the Milky Way, groups like the Pleiades are known as *galactic clusters.**

The Hyades. — Not all galactic clusters, however, resemble the Pleiades. In Taurus we see the Hyades (Plate 31), an even more conspicuous cluster of stars, which, with the bright star Aldebaran, make up the nose of the celestial Bull. Here again is a party of stars, close together in space, traveling in company. Aldebaran is not of

* Sometimes they are known as *open clusters*, to distinguish them from the more compact *globular clusters*, which, as we shall see, are also members of our stellar system, but do not travel the lanes of the Milky Way, or *galaxy*.

the party; he happens to be in direct line between us and them, so that we see him among them, but his motion is not the same.

The Hyades, like the Pleiades, comprise a couple of hundred stars. If we could line them up beside the sun, we should notice two striking differences from the Pleiades. The brightest members are not more than a hundred times as bright as the sun, and not nearly as hot as the brightest Pleiades, and the family portraits of the two clusters are not identical. There are, it is true, a large number of stars in the Hyades — the great majority, in fact — that toe the line of the main sequence. But there are some that fall very far from it. The Hyades contain several red-giant stars (indeed they are its brightest members), far larger than the sun, or than the brightest blue stars in the cluster. The red giants are not numerous — main-sequence stars are still the rule — but there is no doubt about their presence. We begin to detect a variety, in this group of stars of similar age and history, that recalls the variety shown by the double stars, main-sequence stars teamed up not only with main-sequence stars, but also with stars of greater size and lower density.

Some of the Hyades are actually twin systems — double stars within a star cluster. When we look for bright nebulosity such as enmeshes the Pleiades, we look in vain. The Hyades are not tangled in any visible silver braid. None the less, there is some evidence of dark material scattered among the stars. Only hot stars can send back the light of dark nebulosity and show a bright cloud: none of the Hyades is hot enough to do so. But there is little doubt that they, too, move in a cloud of dust.

Hyades and Pleiades show the typical family portraits of all the galactic clusters. Always we find a backbone of main-sequence stars that runs from hot, large, bright stars to cool, small, and faint ones. Combined with this backbone we find varying proportions of cool giants — sometimes a few, as with the Hyades, sometimes more, sometimes, as with the Pleiades, apparently none at all.

The Double Cluster in Perseus. — Among the most beautiful of galactic clusters is the twin cluster in the constellation Perseus (Plate 32). This pair of clusters is so remote that its distance is hard to measure, and even today we are not sure exactly how far away it is. We do know that its brightest stars are among the most luminous known, between ten thousand and a hundred thousand times as bright as the sun. The backbone of its main sequence runs up to stars as bright as this, and at temperatures far higher than those of the brightest Pleiades. So remote are these two clusters that we have not yet observed stars in them that are of the sun's brightness, though we have no reason to doubt that such stars are there. But the most amazing feature of the family portrait of the twin clusters in Perseus is the great group of red supergiants that it contains — a couple of dozen stars as large and as luminous as the great red components of the giant eclipsing stars like Zeta Aurigae and VV Cephei (Fig. 7). The bright, hot stars form compact twin nuclei in a larger system that surrounds the two clusters with a great aura of red stars.

The double cluster in Perseus is deep in nebulosity; one of the problems of measuring its distance is to circumvent the obscuring effect of the clouds that enfold it. And its brightest stars glow with the light that tells of enormous chromospheres or prominences; perhaps they are spilling matter into space; perhaps, too, they are drawing into themselves the clouds in which they lie.

We know of several hundred galactic clusters. All lie in the great traffic way of the Milky Way, all are parties of stars that are moving in company. Each is a true family, of common origin and similar history. Because they move in the central lane, where dust and fog lie thick, we see only those nearest to us — perhaps 10 percent of the whole. We may picture several thousand such clusters moving around the Milky Way, hundreds of thousands of members of these stellar groups, all with family portraits that are similar in general outline, but different in the proportion of stars of various brightnesses, sizes, and colors. The main sequences of galactic clusters extend down to stars that are small, faint, and red; but the numbers do not increase rapidly as we pass down the sequence. In other words, the population of a galactic cluster is like that of the unattached stars of our neighborhood in the *kinds* of stars represented, but not in their *relative numbers*.

Clusters like the Pleiades and Hyades strike our eye because they are more densely packed with stars than the regions in which they lie. There are some that are so widely scattered that we recognize them only because all their members are at about the same distance from us, and move through space in the same direction and at the same speed. Most of the stars of the Big Dipper form a real cluster, and only because we are almost within it do we fail to see that Sirius belongs to the party also. This group, which is known as the Ursa Major cluster, has the family portrait typical of a galactic cluster.

Even more widely spaced are the groups of stars that have been called "stellar associations" by the Russian astronomer Ambartsumian. They seem to form loose groups that are scattered among a much larger number of noncluster stars. Most of the hot, highly luminous stars, which are spraying material around them into space, seem to belong to these "associations." The members seem to be distributed in a vast volume around one or more compact galactic clusters. In fact, Ambartsumian sees an association in the great aura of supergiants that enfolds the double cluster in Perseus.

If these associations of hot, bright stars are real physical groups, as the evidence strongly suggests, they are families of stars of similar origin and history, just as the galactic clusters are. They seem to represent only the brightest section of the family portrait, and the lower part of the main sequence is represented only in the compact clusters on which they center. They must represent a different history, or a different epoch of life, from clusters like the Pleiades.

Numerous as they are, the well-defined galactic clusters comprise but a small fraction of all the stellar travelers. Perhaps one in a thousand of the stars on the circular track belongs to a recognizable galactic cluster; even fewer are members of associations. Very likely there are many smaller clusters that do not strike the eye. We should perhaps not draw a hard-and-fast line between the compact Trapezium and the system of Castor with its six stars grouped in three close pairs, or between the system of Castor and those of Alpha Centauri, Gamma Virginis, and Sirius. The division between visual, spectroscopic, and eclipsing stars is an artificial one based on method of discovery, not on the nature of the thing discovered. In fact, associated systems of stars probably run all the way from the richest galactic clusters down to the close pairs of eclipsing stars.

Weight is given to this view by putting together all the family portraits of galactic clusters into one master portrait, and comparing it with the composite family portrait made from all known double and multiple stars. The general outlines have an extraordinary similarity. Double stars include every type of known star. True, the

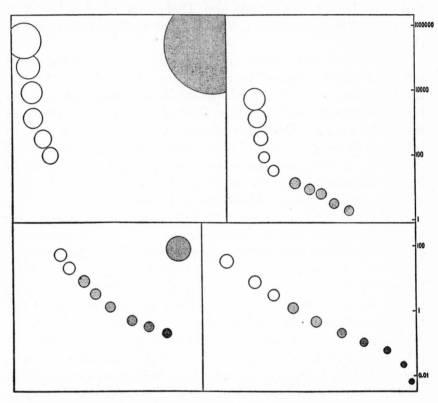

Fig. 8. *Family portraits for three galactic clusters: top left, the twin Perseus clusters; top right, the Pleaides; bottom left, the Hyades. At the bottom, right, is shown a typical selection of nearby non-cluster stars. The sizes of the stars are on a conventional scale. No attempt has been made to show all the stars in any one cluster, but the whole observed range is represented. Numbers on the right show the brightness in terms of the sun. Shading indicates temperature, as in the other figures.*

portraits of galactic clusters seem short on white dwarfs, and even on faint main-sequence stars — but this is more than likely to be an accident of position: few galactic clusters are near enough to us to reveal such members, even if they were present; a few white dwarfs are known members of galactic clusters, such as the Hyades and the Perseus clusters.

72

The same process can even be carried a little further. We possess a great deal of information about the individual stars that lie near to us in space. For these, too, we can compile a general family portrait, and when we do so, a striking fact emerges: the picture of our fellow travelers in the galactic traffic stream is very like those that were put together from the members of galactic clusters and double stars (Fig. 8). The rich variety of stellar individuals is all represented in the picture posed for us by double stars, multiple stars, and galactic clusters.

The vast concourse of stars — tens or hundreds of millions — that are moving around the galactic track forms a great family, and we are gradually piecing together the family portrait. We can go a step further. We can count the numbers of stars that occupy different parts of the portrait, find which are frequent, which are uncommon. When we have made allowance for the effects of distance (which causes us to overestimate the numbers of bright stars at first glance) we find that among our near neighbors *most of the stars in the portrait are fainter, smaller, cooler than the sun.* Brighter stars become progressively rarer; giants are infrequent (especially yellow giants such as Capella) and supergiants so exceptional that they are practically negligible in the total count. We should note again that in galactic clusters the faint, cool stars do not seem to be nearly so numerous as they are in the general star field.

So common are the noncluster stars fainter than the sun that most of the light from the nearby family of stars comes from them. The individual supergiants radiate a great deal; but they are so scarce that their total contribution is only a small fraction of the whole. We are inside our own system of stars, and are apt to miss the significance of this fact; but when we scan a very distant stellar system of similar make-up to our own (and, as we shall see, there are millions of such systems) it is important to keep in mind that most of its light probably comes from stars too faint to be seen.

The group of stars whose portrait we have just drawn, the group that moves mainly in the great circular track of the Milky Way, is only one family of stars. There are other stars, the stellar jaywalkers, that have very different motions, different distribution, and different properties. In order to make a broad general distinction between the two groups, they are often called "Population I" and "Population II." Population I is the group that we have studied; we have seen its typical family portrait, have described its regular motion around the galactic track in the stellar traffic lane that is thick with

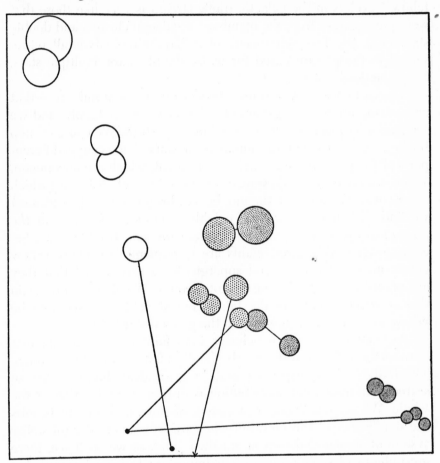

Fig. 9a. *Relations between members of visual double stars. The single stars with white-dwarf companions are Sirius and Procyon; the three stars joined are the components of o² Eridani. The giant pair is Capella. The sizes are on a conventional scale.*

dust and smoke. The stars that cross the great rotary in all directions are known as "Population II." * Our next task will be to sketch the

* The names "Population I and II" were originally given by Baade to the two groups of stars. As we shall see, they probably represent extremes rather than an absolute distinction.

family portrait of this second group of stars, and to see whether the remarkable differences between the two populations can be related to any differences in birth, history, or age.

Globular Clusters. — In the constellation Centaurus, the Cen-

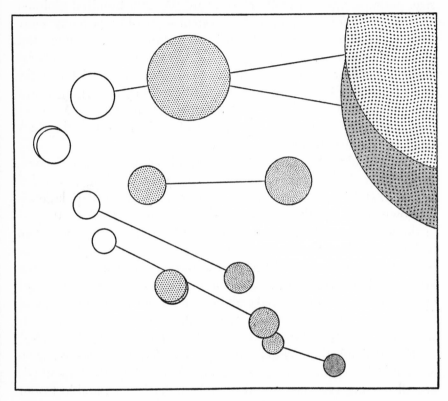

Fɪɢ. 9b. *Relations between members of eclipsing pairs. Associated stars are joined by straight lines. The sizes are on a conventional scale; shading indicates temperature. (Based on a study by S. Gaposchkin.)*

taur, is a dim, hazy naked-eye object that was named as a star — Omega Centauri (Plates 37 and 38). Under the telescope it appears as one of the most magnificent objects in the sky. It is evidently a gigantic ball of stars (very slightly flattened, perhaps rotating), and its numbers are beyond estimate — certainly hundreds of thousands, possibly millions. Numerous as are the stars that can be counted, far more are below the limit of observation. The cluster shines with the brightness of nearly a million suns; and if, as in our neighborhood, stars fainter than our sun are in the majority, the population must indeed exceed a million.

Omega Centauri is a typical *globular cluster*, over the average in size, perhaps, and unusually close to us. About a hundred globular clusters are known in our stellar system — possibly as many more have escaped observation because of distance or dimming. But globular clusters are not so generally hidden from us as galactic clusters, for they do not cling to the central dust layer of the Milky Way. Instead of being confined to a flat layer, they are arranged in a nearly spherical group that outlines our system of stars. Many of them are, so to speak, seen overhead, rather than through the thick layer of dust that blankets our flat traffic way.

The globular clusters lie far above and below the central layer, and their paths intersect it at all angles. They are huge, crowded parties of stars that move athwart the circular paths of Population I. Our own rapid circular motion makes us seem to approach them — or them to approach us — from one direction. As a group they seem to be going the opposite way. But that is an illusion. Just as an object seen from a moving train seems to be flying backward, so the group of globular clusters as a whole seems to be moving backward at great speed. When we make allowance for our own motion round the galactic rotary, the system of globular clusters (as a whole) is seen to have little rotation — little motion round the traffic circle.*

Even though the globular clusters, considered as a group, seem to have little rotational motion round the Milky Way, the individuals are all moving very fast — with speeds, indeed, comparable to our own speed around the track — but in all possible directions. They cut across our path at all angles, and their almost spherical distribution is the result. We shall find that other individual stars that do not follow our traffic lane are distributed in similar ways; the less they obey the rule of the rotary, the more are they distributed in a thick system that approaches the spherical, instead of in the thin layer that lies within the central filling of dust.

---

* Whether the globular clusters, as a group, possess *any* total rotational motion is a difficult question to answer; their distribution, among other things, suggests that at least they have rather little.

Let us line up the members of a globular cluster for a family portrait. Omega Centauri, unfortunately, has never posed, but several of the northern globular clusters, such as the Great Cluster in Hercules, have been carefully portrayed. The composite picture is very unlike that of a galactic cluster (Fig. 10). The brightest stars are less than a thousand times as bright as the sun, much inferior to the bright members of galactic clusters. And — more striking still —

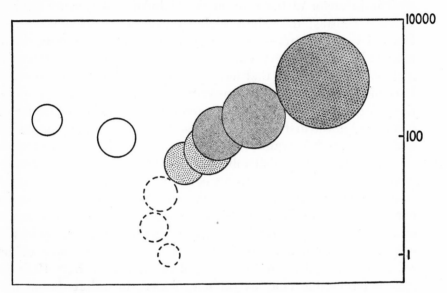

Fig. 10. *Typical family portrait for a globular cluster. Broken circles are somewhat conjectural. The great majority of the bright stars in the cluster follow the line that runs diagonally from the top right to the lower left; only a few are shown. The sizes are on a conventional scale. Brightness, in terms of the sun, is indicated on the right.*

the brightest stars are the reddest, coolest, and largest, not the bluest and hottest, as in the Pleiades. A few globular clusters do contain some blue stars, but they are most exceptional — more so than the red giants in galactic clusters. The contrast between the family portraits of globular and galactic clusters is unmistakable. There are differences of detail, too, on which we need not for the moment dwell — differences that show that surface conditions of the stars, as well as gross appearance, differ between the two populations.

Very recent studies of globular clusters, by Arp, Baum, and Sandage, have contained a most significant suggestion. The brighter

77

stars lie on a sequence that runs from bright, large, red toward fainter, smaller, cooler stars, as Shapley showed many years since. In fact it seems to run in a direction almost opposite to that of the main sequence that forms the backbone of the family portrait for a galactic cluster. The new results show that it draws near to the main sequence for stars a little fainter than the sun, and below this point the two portraits seem to run together.

The behavior of the stars in the globular and galactic clusters shows a contrast too. Many globular clusters are rich in certain kinds of variable stars — the rapidly pulsing "RR Lyrae stars," with periods less than a day, and the more slowly pulsing "RV Tauri" and "W Virginis" stars that have peculiar light curves and spectra. Variable stars are practically unknown in galactic clusters. Population I does, indeed, include some variable stars, such as the Cepheids mentioned in the first chapter; but the kinds of variables common in globular clusters are quite foreign to Population I.

The variable stars that inhabit globular clusters differ from one system to another. Some clusters contain over a hundred RR Lyrae stars, others few or none; and the distribution of the vibration periods also differs from cluster to cluster. The Mount Wilson study of family portraits strongly suggests that different variable-star peculiarities are linked with differences in the precise course of the red-to-blue, bright-to-faint branches of the family portraits. Here we have a fascinating clue, as yet unexploited, to differences of age and history between globular clusters.

Even Omega Centauri, one of the nearest of all globular clusters, is so far away that stars as bright as the sun are difficult to observe there, and stars much fainter are quite inaccessible. We have no reason to doubt that such stars are commonest in the globular clusters, just as in our own district. But at present our knowledge of their numbers and properties is most exiguous. My own belief is that the family portraits of globular and galactic clusters, so unlike for the brighter stars, will be found to merge for the faint ones; that the two types of cluster, and the populations that they typify, rest, so to speak, on the same base, and fan out differently only higher up. And I will anticipate the conclusion of a later chapter, and hazard that the difference in the manner of fanning out is a matter of age: the globular clusters (Population II) show the portrait of a much older family of stars than the galactic clusters (Population I). Bright stars do not wear as well as faint ones. Very luminous stars, the stellar prodigals, exhaust themselves early; faint stars, less luminous than the sun, husband their resources so that they continue to shine with little alteration from age to age. The basis for this conclusion must be left for a later chapter.

We saw that the family portrait of the galactic clusters is reproduced by the composite picture of all the stars that are moving round the galactic rotary. There is another group of stars that give a composite picture very like that of the globular clusters — the individual stars that are moving *across* the galactic track, the "high-velocity stars."

Most stars in our neighborhood move nearly in the same way as the sun, circling the galaxy within the central sandwich of dust and haze. But some stars, like the globular clusters, cut across our path at all angles. They, too, *seem* all to be moving in one direction, because we see in them the reflection of our own motion round the circle. Actually they are threading the stellar system in all directions and at all angles. We call them the "high-velocity stars," though actually their speeds are no higher than the sun's. But we are moving with the main stream of traffic, and their motions, athwart our own, loom large because they are in a different direction.

These high-velocity stars include many sorts. When we piece them together into a composite portrait, we get something much more like the picture of the globular cluster than that of the galactic cluster. The variable stars of the kinds common in the globular clusters, when found by themselves, all prove to be high-velocity stars. Because they cut across the central layer at all sorts of angles, they are seen at a variety of heights above it. There is no doubt that they constitute a great globular haze of stars all round the central dust layer, and little doubt that they really make up the bulk of the population of our stellar system. This latter fact is far from obvious to us, for the traffic round the rotary is fairly dense in our vicinity — denser than the haze of jaywalkers. But in some parts of our stellar system the high-velocity stars are far more densely crowded, and the rotary traffic all but nonexistent. We might, in fact, scarcely suspect this to be the case if we had observed stars within our system only. But when we look across the emptiness of space at other systems that are very like our own, we see the two populations in their true proportions — rotary traffic limited to restricted lanes, and a gigantic globe of Population II stars that surrounds and pervades everything. These distant views of other stellar systems, and the comparison with our own, will be the theme of the next chapter.

The galactic clusters, it will be remembered, move in the layer of dust and atoms, and often illuminate or irradiate the interstellar clouds. No such environment seems to pervade the globular clusters. They show no sign of dark, obscuring material, and no nebular atoms glow within them. Probably these great clusters of stars are nearly, or quite, free of interstellar material. As we shall learn in a later chapter, this difference of environment has probably been a potent factor in their development.

5   Systems of Stars

We have met the individual members of the cast of our cosmic drama: stars, dust, and gas. We have studied intimate situations: double stars, multiple stars, clusters of stars. Let us look at some panoramas of the whole stage, arrested in a moment of action.

Almost all the players that we have hitherto met are members of our own stellar system. Our system of stars is one among millions, by no means all alike. What would it look like if we could survey it from a point outside it?

Our stellar system is very difficult to survey, and in the second chapter we have already seen the reason for the difficulty. The sun moves in the main trafficway, which is thick with a ground fog of dust, haze, and interstellar smoke. Comparatively nearby stars in the central layer are obscured by the fog, and the more distant parts are hidden altogether. The problem of surveying our own stellar system is as hard as that of making a map of a large and smoky city from one point in the thick of the traffic.

A beginning can be made by counting the stars of different brightnesses that are seen in different directions. Many millions of stars are accessible with modern telescopes, and to count all of them would be impossible and unnecessary; one chooses a number of sample regions for the census. But the census is only the first step; if we are to find out from our sample counts how many stars the whole system contains, we must make allowance for the number obscured or cut off by the fog.

Even this is not so easy as it sounds. Faint stars seen in any direction may be faint for several reasons. Perhaps they really shine very feebly, like Proxima Centauri, which we see only because it is extremely near to us. Perhaps they are very bright, but extremely distant from us. Or perhaps they are behind one or more patches of fog, and therefore nearer to us than they seem. This is actually the case for all very luminous, distant stars, and allowance must be made for it in mapping our stellar system, the galaxy.

The distances of a very few stars can be measured geometrically, if they are close enough to show an appreciable displacement (parallax), which reflects the earth's annual motion round the sun. These stars are most useful, for they furnish the yardstick for more distant ones. If we line up all the stars whose distances can be measured, so that they are seen in their true relation to one another, certain regularities appear. These mass pictures are very like the family portraits of star clusters that we met in the last chapter. Many of the regularities make it possible to tell how bright a star is, for example, if its color (temperature or spectrum) can be ascertained, and if we know to what kind of family it belongs. Both galactic-cluster (Population I) and globular-cluster (Population II) families have their own regularities, and if a star can be assigned to one of them, its properties are usually fixed, its brightness and distance are known, and it can be placed in the map.

The whole difficulty lies in assigning the star to the right population; and here the star's motion may be called in to settle the question. Population I stars are going round the circular track. Members of Population II tend to be high-velocity stars, which are crossing the track at all angles. The motion separates the stars only roughly, for a few stars of Population II may happen to be moving with the stream, but for a vast number of stars whose distances cannot otherwise be determined, it enables us to place them in the mass portrait, to determine what they are like and therefore where they are.

The laborious patching together of information on the properties and motions of stars within our stellar system gives a fairly clear picture of the whole. The great complex of stars within which the sun moves has a comparatively thin central layer — the dusty, smoky filling of the cake (to use the simile of the second chapter).

The filling is probably circular, and about a hundred thousand light-years across from edge to edge. Its thickness is very small in comparison — between two and three thousand light-years, little more than 2 percent of its width. The sun is at a great distance from the center — nearly thirty thousand light-years — and less than twenty thousand light-years from the edge.

The rotary stream of stellar traffic moves within the thin circular layer of filling. The sun takes about two hundred million years to travel once round the track. Stars farther from the center than the sun take even longer; stars nearer the center, which move rather faster, make the circuit in a shorter time. These differences in speed round the rotary, small as they are, constitute our evidence for the motions within the stream of stellar traffic.

The layer of filling, and the stars that move in it, mark the course of the Milky Way — the hazy band of light that runs round the sky and is resolved by the telescope into myriads of stars, variegated by patches of dust and by luminous nebulae that scatter or transform the starlight.

If there were no dust or haze in the layer that marks the Milky Way, the direction toward the center of the system (in the constellations Sagittarius and Ophiuchus) would shine with a blaze of light as compared with the direction toward the edge nearest to us (in Taurus and Canis Major). The dust lies particularly thick in the direction of the center itself, and hides the nucleus of our stellar system from eye and photograph; but redder light comes through more easily (it is scattered less), and with radio waves, or even infrared light, the central regions begin to give a hint of their true brilliance.

Even though we cannot see the great bulk of stars toward the center of our system, there are plenty of clues (when we know where to look for them) that show that we are really nearer the edge. Stars with the earmarks of high luminosity are observed at distances of thirty thousand light-years, and more, in the direction of the center — but no such luminous distant stars are to be seen in the opposite direction.

The traffic density is not the same in all parts of the great rotary. On the whole the stars grow denser as we look toward the hub of the system, the nucleus about which the galaxy turns. But the star density has definite ups and downs in both directions. It was the Dutch astronomer Oort and the Swedish astronomer Lindblad who first recognized the rotary motion in our system for what it is; and it was Oort who also noticed that the circular stream of traffic has its densely crowded lanes, with more sparsely traveled zones between them. We seem to be on the inner edge of one thickly traveled zone, and another, even more populous, runs nearer the nucleus of our galaxy.

Other galaxies, as we shall see, display similar variations of the traffic density, which are disposed in graceful spiral coils about their nuclei. Most astronomers believe that even in our own system there is evidence of *spiral arms*, that lie coiled in the central filling and move within it. Actual spiral structure within the galaxy is difficult to trace by mapping the distribution of stars; we can see the details only in small segments of the circle, and even these are broken up by the patches of nearby obscuring matter. But most of the patchwork map that we have been able to construct fits into the spiral pattern if we are careful to choose the right stars in making it.

The travelers par excellence around the central track are the stars of Population I, which we met in the last chapter. The rotational motion in the galaxy is shown best of all by the hot, luminous stars that occupy the upper part of the main sequence — such stars as the brightest Pleiades, and the high-temperature members of the great Double Cluster of Perseus. Our most reliable information about the rotation of the galaxy was obtained from this group of stars by the Canadian astronomers J. S. Plaskett and Joseph Pearce.

The highly luminous, hot stars are a natural choice for such a study, because they are visible at immense distances, and the details of their spectra make possible (with the necessary precautions) the measurement of these distances, which are essential ingredients of the picture. The principal precaution that must be taken is the allowance for dimming by obscuring material, a serious factor for just this group of stars, because they lie, almost without exception, within the central layer of dust and fog. The dimming can be measured, in the manner described in Chapter 2, by the amount of reddening that it produces. The delicate precision of the photoelectric cell has been applied to these measures by Stebbins and his associates, with the result that we know the true distances of over a thousand of the hot, luminous stars — a better showing than for a comparable sample of stars of any other kind.

But we did not choose the hot, luminous stars to survey the spiral structure of our galaxy only because they are readily singled out. They actually follow the spiral structure more closely than stars of any other kind. If our observations were confined to our own galaxy we might not have realized this extremely important fact; but it is forced upon us by the study of other galaxies that are near enough for us to recognize similar stars there. The arms of the great galaxy in Andromeda are traced out, as we shall see, by the bright, high-temperature stars. Here we have one of the cardinal facts of stellar evolution, and we shall explore some of its consequences later.

These hot supergiant stars have effects on their environment. The great Nebula of Orion is but one of innumerable gas clouds that are illuminated and stimulated to a brilliant glow by hot stars that lie within them. The omnipresent gas that drifts within the central layer of the galaxy will betray its presence if a high-temperature supergiant is near enough to call forth the nebular spectrum from its atoms.

When the spiral structure of our galaxy was surveyed in the light of the nebulae that wreathe the hot supergiants, it began to stand out for the first time in clear and spectacular fashion. Quite recently W. W. Morgan and his associates at the Yerkes Observatory, by an ingenious and beautiful technique, have actually photographed the course of the spiral arms of our galaxy in nebular light. For the first time the arms stand out clearly; Morgan has delineated two for a distance of some six thousand light-years, and located a probable third. A picture that was only vaguely sketched before begins to take definite outlines.

The bright nebulae shine because hot stars are near them, and no doubt great tracts of interstellar gas remain unseen because they lack a stimulating star. But the affiliation is no mere accident. For what we know of the motions of the bright nebulae tells us that they, too, are coursing round the circular track with speed similar to that of the stars. There is a connection between hot supergiants and nebulae scarcely less intimate than that between groups of stars that are moving in company. Of the probable cause and possible effects of the relation we shall speak in a later chapter.

The hot, bright stars display the galactic rotation more clearly than any other group. But there are other luminous stars, which are restricted to the central layer of the galaxy, and share the rotational motion. Such are the Cepheid variables, the pulsing stars that we met in the first chapter. They are certainly members of Population I. They lie in the central layer, and Joy, at Mount Wilson, has shown definitely that they move around the circular track.

Cepheid variables, however, are not such dyed-in-the-wool members of Population I as the high-temperature supergiants. We look for them in vain in the galactic clusters and in the stellar associations of Ambartsumian. It is true that Cepheid variables are scarce in the galaxy; perhaps there is one Cepheid to half a million stars of Population I. But the hot supergiants are at least as scarce, and they are well represented in the galactic clusters.

The five hundred Cepheids that are known at present can be spotted on the map of the galaxy, but not, it is true, as accurately as the hot stars. We know their true brightness from the period-luminosity relation, but when we try to correct their distances for obscurations we run into a more difficult problem, or at least a bigger one. Much work must be done before we know their true colors, and can measure how much they are reddened, for their changing brightness multiplies enormously the labor of determining both these things. Here again we must depend on the delicate methods of photoelectric photometry.

The map that shows the probable positions of the Cepheids within the galaxy does not show the clear-cut spiral structure that is revealed by the bright nebulae and by the hot supergiants. It is as if the Cepheids are spread out into a sheet while the supergiants are distributed in definite lanes. The sheet is a thin one, for the Cepheids hug the plane of the galaxy; but for them the clear-cut spiral structure seems blurred.

Stars of Population I are not confined to the luminous stars, either the hot supergiants or the Cepheids. They comprise the fainter associated stars that people the main sequence in enormous numbers as far as the very cool dwarfs. Most stars in our neighborhood belong to this family, and move round the circular track. Perhaps a thousand million galactic stars inhabit, and move in, the central filling of the galaxy. But none seem to show the structural pattern as clearly as those that inhabit the upper end of the main sequence.

But the stars in the central layer are not the only — indeed perhaps not the most important — part of our galactic system. The high-velocity stars represent Population II — the typical globular-cluster family. Here are no spendthrift stars; the brightest have little more than a hundred times the sun's luminosity. Here are no bright, hot stars, no Wolf-Rayet stars, no Cepheid variables. But the population teems with RR Lyrae stars, which pulsate in hours rather than days. It contains subgiants, it contains subdwarfs, and apparently its fainter members are indistinguishable (save by position and motion) from the fainter stars of Population I. Above all, it contains the globular clusters.

By position and speed we distinguish Population II. The reflection of our rotary motion makes them all seem to be traveling one way, but actually they move almost indiscriminately, crossing the central layer at all angles, and therefore reaching to great distances above it and below it. If Population I is a thin central slice, Population II is a spherical or spheroidal haze that encloses the whole. We know of RR Lyrae stars thirty thousand light-years *above* the galactic plane.

The greatest and most spherical system of all is that of the globular clusters, a hundred or more dense globes of stars arranged nearly in a sphere about the galactic system.

To the globular clusters we owe our realization of the immense size of the galactic system, and of our position within it. Only a few decades ago the sun was thought to be at or near the center of a system of stars, a few hundred light-years across. It was Shapley who realized that the globular clusters are grouped about the center of the galaxy; that the system must therefore be tens of thousands of light-years across; and that we must lie far from its center — nearer, indeed, to one of the edges. The broadening of our horizon that resulted from this revelation marked the beginnings of a totally new conception of the universe. Today we talk of, and measure, hundreds of millions of light-years, instead of mere hundreds. The radius of the astronomer's domain has been multiplied by a million in the past half-century; its volume by a million million million.

The globular or spheroidal system of stars that makes up Population II is probably much denser toward the center of our galaxy than in our own neighborhood. We lie near its outer fringes, where its stars are sparsely distributed, and from a glance at our own environs we grossly underestimate their numbers. They probably constitute at least 90 percent of all the inhabitants of the galaxy.

We may think of Population II as a sort of gigantic globular cluster that encircles and includes the whole system, with smaller globular clusters embedded in it. Other galaxies show an enormous increase of star density toward their centers, and there is every reason to think that our own is similar.

In the past few years, surveys have actually been made of regions comparatively close to the nucleus of our galaxy, and they show a very great increase in the density of the typical Population II stars such as the RR Lyrae variables. The planetary nebulae and novae (also probably characteristic of Population II), are found to be greatly concentrated toward the galactic nucleus; and this concentration is doubtless a characteristic of the population as a whole.

The globular haze is really the main body of our stellar system. It is probably without any structure; it does not partake of the condensations that suggest spiral arms. It extends throughout the whole galaxy in a continuous haze of stars. Very likely it comprises ten to a hundred times as many stars as the Population I stars that move within the central layer, perhaps a hundred thousand million. It is the real, permanent population of the galaxy; the stars of the dust lane are few by comparison, perhaps a mere thousand million — and many of them, as we shall see, are (cosmically speaking) ephemeral.

We do not know how close to the center the layer of dust filling extends. We are almost certain that it does not pass right through the center — it is not so much a layer as a sort of doughnut of dust. The center is probably a great, dense globe of Population II stars, essentially free of dust or haze. From observations of our own galaxy we could scarcely make this statement; but comparison with other, similar systems, makes it fairly certain.

The Andromeda Galaxy. — Far from the confines of our galaxy, seen through the stars of Andromeda, lies another great stellar system, about 750,000 light-years away (Plate 39). It was noted more than a hundred years ago by the French astronomer Messier, who was hunting for comets. Messier found that he was bedeviled in his search by a number of hazy-looking objects, which disappointed him by remaining stationary among the stars, as no comet would do. He made a list of objects that should be disregarded by comet seekers; the galaxy in Andromeda was No. 31 of his list of 104 objects. While looking for the smallest and most inconsiderable members of the cosmic population, he calmly set aside about a hundred great systems of stars. His list contains the brightest globular clusters, and also a number of galaxies, many over a million light-years away. They are often identified by the number that he gave them: thus the Andromeda galaxy is frequently known as "Messier 31." In fact, Messier is remembered today for his list of "disappointing objects," rather than for his study of comets.

The galaxy in Andromeda is about as bright as our own, contains nearly as many stars, and is almost as large. Most galaxies are smaller. The progress of astronomy has successively shown that the earth is a small planet, not at the center of the solar system; that the sun is a small star, not at the center of the galaxy; and that our galaxy is only one among billions. We retain but one distinction. We believe that our own stellar system is one of the biggest. Will this proud claim, too, be disallowed by advancing knowledge?

Apart from the small difference in size, the Andromeda galaxy looks from here very much as the galactic system would look from there. It is presented to us nearly on edge. Actually it must be circular, and the fact that we see it in elliptical projection shows that its central layer is tilted toward us at about 75°. An observer there would see our own galaxy more nearly face-on, tipped at about 70°.

The first feature that strikes the eye in the Andromeda galaxy is the coiled spiral arms that wind round the bright center (Plate 40). These are the counterparts of the traffic lanes of our own stellar system. Like them, the spiral arms are moving in a layer of dust and gas, and are studded with bright nebulae. Very luminous blue stars lie in the arms, just as in our own system. Messier 31 is so far away that no star less than a hundred times as bright as the sun can be seen there as an individual. A star as bright as Sirius would be of about the twenty-first magnitude, barely visible on photographs taken with the most powerful telescope. Sunlike stars there are beyond our ken, and probably will be so for a long time to come. All the bright stars in the arms (chiefly hot blue stars like Rigel or Alnitam, or groups of such stars, like the Perseus clusters and the Pleiades), are typical of Population I, and so are the bright nebulae. We see evidence of the central dust sandwich in the streaks of dark material that lie against the bright star groups in the arms. The dust — and the Population I stars — cease abruptly at a point near the bright nucleus, and evidently the central portion, which is by far the most brilliant, is clean of haze and dust.

The spiral arms of the Andromeda galaxy can be rather vaguely made out on an ordinary photograph; but a photograph in hydrogen light, which picks out the bright nebulae, is a revelation. The outer arms, photographed by Baade at Mount Wilson, are marked out clearly, narrow bands studded with the glowing gas near the bright, hot stars, just as the arms of our own galaxy were first definitely outlined in nebular light.

Many bright Cepheids are known in Messier 31. We first realized that this system is a great spiral, hundreds of thousands of light years away, when Hubble discovered these Cepheids and inferred their true brightness from the period-luminosity curve. Up to that time, less than thirty years ago, opinion was divided as to whether the spiral galaxies were small, nearby objects, perhaps even inside our own system, or "island universes" at immense distances. Hubble's discovery opened up a new world of distant systems, which today we count by billions.

The Cepheids discovered by Hubble are among the bright stars of the Andromeda galaxy, and stand out clearly on the structure of the system. We can probably assume that, like the Cepheids of our own galaxy, they lie in a fairly thin central layer. In our own system the Cepheids seem to be spread in a thin sheet, rather than concentrated in the arms, like the hot supergiants, and in Messier 31 also they seem to be distributed *between* the spiral arms. Only since Baade made his spectacular photographs of the delicate narrow coils, studded with bright nebulae, has this been apparent; and it confirms the vaguer impression given by the Cepheid map of our own system.

The bright center of Messier 31 long remained "unresolved"; it had not been seen as consisting of discernible stars (Plate 41). There was no doubt that it actually consisted of stars, not of bright nebulosity; the spectrum was that of stars, and showed none of the bright radiations typical of gaseous nebulae. Evidently the stars were simply too faint to be seen as individuals, fainter than the bright stars of the arms.

The resolution of the central regions of the Andromeda galaxy was one of the great observational feats of the last decade. It was achieved by Baade, at Mount Wilson Observatory. Baade reasoned that if the stars in the nucleus are reddish, they should affect red-sensitive plates more than blue plates; and by a careful choice of plates and exposures, and great dexterity in guiding the telescope, he succeeded in photographing the individual stars of the nucleus, near the limit of the red plates.

The picture of the nucleus shows an unbelievable number of stars, crowded into a structureless mass. "It looks," as one of the first to see it remarked, "like a heap of pepper." The brightest of its stars was nearly at the limit of the 100-inch telescope — a little brighter than Sirius. The fact that they show better in red light than in blue shows that they are reddish. In fact, they are exactly like the brightest stars in the globular clusters, and the whole nucleus of the Andromeda galaxy resembles a globular cluster on an enormous scale, greatly condensed in the center, and distributed about it in a structureless mass that is probably almost spherical.

The nucleus of Messier 31 has other things in common with a globular cluster besides the colors and brightness of its brightest stars. It seems completely free of dust and gas; the absence of gas is seen when the spectrum is examined, and the absence of dust, when the nuclear regions are seen actually to be *transparent!* * Of course,

---

* I am indebted to Dr. Baade for this information.

there are no individual stars to be seen behind the Andromeda galaxy, which is far beyond the confines of our stellar system. But myriads of other stellar systems are even more remote. In the region of the arms such systems are not to be seen because of the obscuring power of the dust in the central layer — but they are seen through the nucleus, and they are also seen between the arms.

How large is the nucleus of the Andromeda galaxy? It extends out to the point where the spiral arms begin; and it is seen again in the spaces between the arms. In fact, it is actually an enormous spheroid of stars that enfolds the whole system, arms and all. The peppering of stars (less dense than in the central regions) pervades the whole system. We are reminded of the great haze of Population II stars that underlies the entire structure of our galaxy, and we cannot doubt that the great mass of stars that underlies the structure of Messier 31 is of exactly the same nature. They have all the properties of Population II: the brightest stars are also the reddest, and they are not accompanied by interstellar dust or gas.

A careful study of the brightness of the arms of the Andromeda galaxy, as compared with the brightness of the Population II substratum, shows without question that the Population II stars form the immense majority. The arms show up because they contain individual bright stars and nebulae; but the bulk of the stars, very likely 99 percent of them (mostly invisible to us as individuals), belongs to the underlying substratum, which extends in a structureless haze throughout the entire system.

Comparison of the transparency of the arms and the regions that lie between them contributes another fact that we should hardly have discovered from a study of our own stellar system. There is no obscuration *between* the arms; the densely peppered intermediate regions are quite transparent, and distant galaxies show through them undimmed. Very likely our own system has similar structure; dust and smoke and interstellar gas are really confined to the stellar traffic ways, which are separated by clean regions. The point that Population I stars like the hot supergiants are invariably associated with dust and gas, and that they do not occur in dustless regions, is made with convincing force.

If the underlying substratum of the galaxy in Andromeda consists of Population II stars, we should expect it to be rich in the objects that are most typical of that population in the galaxy — the globular clusters and the rapidly pulsing RR Lyrae stars. Globular clusters are bright — from ten thousand times to a million times as bright as our sun — and easily seen at the distance of Messier 31. About two hundred of them have been found in the system, and distant though they be, they can be seen to have the slightly fuzzy outlines that show them to be star clusters. They have the same color as our own globular clusters, and about the same brightness,* and without doubt they are arranged, like our own, in an almost spherical system about the great spiral.

The RR Lyrae stars are more difficult to detect, as they are about at the limit of detectability with the means by which the nucleus was first resolved. Very recent information, however, obtained with the greater resources of the 200-inch telescope, reveals vast numbers of variable stars within the nucleus, and although these have not yet received detailed analysis, there is a possibility that the RR Lyrae stars of the substratum have been reached.†

Our present knowledge of the Andromeda galaxy is not confined to analysis of its structure. Luckily for us, it is tipped toward us in such a way that its rotation can be measured. The form suggests a pinwheel, and the spectroscope shows that Messier 31 is indeed spinning rapidly, and in a rather complex way. The rotation is not like that of a wheel, in which the whole structure turns like a solid body and maintains its shape. The motion of the central portion is indeed wheellike; but the outer portions show differential motions that are faster as we recede from the center, and fall off again at the extreme edge. Clearly the system cannot maintain its shape, and the arms must be gradually twisting into new forms as time goes on.

How will the unequal rotation change the shape of Messier 31? Curiously enough, although the reality and size of the rotational

* There is actually rather a puzzling difference of about a magnitude in the average brightness; but this may be a result of slight uncertainty in our determination of the distances either of the galactic globular clusters or of those in Messier 31, which have necessarily been made hitherto by rather different methods.

† If this proves to be true, the distance of Messier 31 will be determined without uncertainty, and the problem of the brightness of its globular clusters, as compared to those of the galaxy, will be resolved at once.

motions is admitted by everybody, there is a great difference of opinion as to how the structure is actually changing. The reason is that *we cannot tell from mere inspection which edge of the system is nearer to us.* If the edge that shows the darkest lanes is nearer, the outer arms are trailing behind, and the system is winding its spiral arms more closely with time. But if the other edge is the nearer, the spirals are unwinding and the outer arms are going ahead.

Most astronomers, I believe (and I am of their number), think that the dark lanes that run across the edge of the nucleus are on the near side; but there is also weighty opinion to the contrary. Some additional evidence is furnished by the globular clusters: if we take them to form a spherical system, those that lie behind the obscuration of the arms, as seen from our position, should be fainter, on the whole, than those that lie on this side of the central dust layer. The evidence of the globular clusters agrees with that given by the central obscurations that seem to be projected against the nucleus, and indicate that the spiral is winding itself up, with the outer arms trailing. The question, as we shall see in a later chapter, is fundamental to an understanding of the development of spiral galaxies, and therefore of the stars of which they are made.

No account of Messier 31 is complete without mention of the novae, or new stars, that have appeared in it. One supernova was observed in 1885 — the closest supernova of modern times. These colossal explosions, in which a giant star seems to be almost completely demolished, are one of the great puzzles of astronomy, and we have made too little progress in solving it, chiefly because recent supernovae have been far off and faint, so that the crucial studies of their spectra were hard to make. The supernova in Messier 31 was of the sixth magnitude, and if it appeared today it would probably lead to a complete solution of the mystery. It is an ironic thought that if this spiral were only 0.1 percent farther from us than it is, the light of the supernova would have spent longer on its travels, and would not have arrived until we had the resources of modern spectroscopy at our command!

Besides the supernova, about a hundred "ordinary" novae have been found in the system during the past quarter of a century, largely through the work of Hubble, as many as have been recorded in the whole history of our own galaxy. If we make allowance for the fact that some novae in our own system have been missed, it seems that new stars are about equally common in the two systems. In our own galaxy the novae seem to belong to Population II (though this is still open to some debate), and in Messier 31 they seem to be distributed more or less like the Population II objects; for example, the majority have appeared in the nuclear regions, where no Cepheid variables, typical of Population I, have occurred. It seems, however, that the novae, both in our galaxy and in the Andromeda galaxy, are distributed in a system more flattened and less spherical than that of the globular clusters.

On the whole, our own galaxy and Messier 31 seem to be very similar in structure and in population. They seem to be about equally bright; our own system is apparently rather larger (though Messier 31 can be seen, with special means, to extend far beyond the confines that appear on an ordinary photograph), and rather more massive. In our own system, there is a mass of perhaps one or two hundred thousand million suns; in Messier 31, perhaps half as much; but this conclusion is necessarily very tentative.

The Companions of the Andromeda Galaxy. — The Andromeda galaxy is not an isolated system; it has two (probably four) faint companion galaxies, of which the two brightest are conspicuous on all photographs of the system itself. All four are much smaller and much less luminous; but the difference does not end there.

The companions to the Andromeda galaxy are quite structureless (Plates 44 and 50). They have no spiral arms, they contain practically no dust or gas, and they are of beautifully symmetrical form. Such systems, which are very common in space, are called, from their appearance, *elliptical galaxies.* For a long time they remained unresolved into stars; but from their spectra there was no doubt that they were purely stellar.

The feat of resolving the companions to Messier 31 was achieved by Baade at the same time as the resolution of its own nucleus, and their population proved to be exactly similar. They consist of Population II stars only, and (save for dimensions and brightness) they resemble gigantic globular clusters.

This statement must be slightly qualified. A few isolated patches of obscuration are seen; within them, *and there only*, blue stars typical of Population I are found.

The association of Messier 31 with several systems so different in size, brightness, and structure reminds us inevitably of the strange bedfellows among the stars. There is a real analogy. The huge, bright galaxies like Messier 31 are conspicuous, but the small, structureless ones that are found teamed up with them are probably the immense majority, just as stars fainter than the sun outnumber stars like Rigel, or even like Sirius, in the galactic population. The problem posed for galactic evolution is exactly parallel to that for stellar development; and I have no doubt that when the one is solved, the solution of the other will inevitably follow.

Irregular Galaxies. – The Andromeda galaxy is not unique in possessing companions that contrast sharply with it. Our own galaxy has two companions of a very different kind – the so-called Magellanic Clouds, visible (alas) only from the southern hemisphere. No greater contrast with the companions of Messier 31 could be imagined.

The Magellanic Clouds are *irregular galaxies* (Plates 45, 46, and 47). They have none of the symmetry of the elliptical galaxies, and they can hardly be called structureless, though they show no beautiful spiral coils. They are rich in clusters of stars, and their density varies from place to place, in a way quite different from that of Messier 31.

The Large Magellanic Cloud is an enormous system, above the average galaxy in size and brightness. It has a dense central region, and shows numerous bright stars and star clusters, some bedded in bright nebulosity (Plate 48). Moreover, Shapley has shown that it obscures the light of more distant galaxies, and there is no doubt that it is full of dust and gas. The Small Magellanic Cloud is more transparent, therefore less dusty, and shows less bright nebulosity, and it, too, is rich in bright stars.

The pride of the Magellanic Clouds is their population of Cepheid variables, far commoner, in proportion to total population, than in the arms of our own galaxy or of Messier 31. These Cepheid variables belong to history, for it was by means of them that the famous *period-luminosity curve*, the yardstick for more distant galaxies, was first discovered and put to use.

Equally striking is the richness of the Magellanic Clouds in blue supergiants — spendthrifts that leave most of our galactic supergiants in the shade. One of the brightest, S Doradus (perhaps a twin system), is a million times as bright as the sun. Thousands of stars in the Clouds are true supergiants. With our present facilities, we can reach stars about half as bright as Sirius in the Magellanic Clouds.

All the members of the Magellanic population that we have mentioned are objects characteristic of Population I: bright, hot supergiants, Cepheid variables, nebulosity, dust. Indeed it looks as if we have here a pure specimen of that population, unmixed with any hint of Population II. The touchstone for Population II is the occurrence of globular clusters and of RR Lyrae stars. Do the Clouds give any evidence of their presence?

The Large Cloud contains a number of beautiful, compact star clusters, many of which look like the globular clusters of our galaxy, and have indeed about the same total brightness. They do, in fact, suggest the presence of the second population. That, however, is not quite certain. Recent work, done by Thackeray at the Radcliffe Observatory in South Africa, shows definitely that though these clusters look like globular clusters, their stars show the family portrait characteristic of galactic clusters: the brightest stars are the bluest. In color and dimensions, therefore, the component stars are of Population I, though the compactness of the clusters suggests Population II.

Concerning the RR Lyrae stars our information is more definite. We can reach stars fainter than the RR Lyrae type in both Clouds, and yet not one member of this distinctive group has been discovered there among the thousands of variable stars that are known. We see vast numbers of Cepheids; we see eclipsing stars and red variables — but there are no RR Lyrae stars. Novae, too, are exceedingly uncommon, though a very few have been discovered; and novae, as we have seen, are very likely members of Population II.

Our series of panoramas of the whole stage has necessarily been limited to a few. We have looked at the picture presented by the galaxy — stellar traffic lanes that are probably spiral arms, and an underlying haze of Population II stars. The great spiral in Andromeda presents a panorama, very much as our own galaxy would look from the outside — spiral arms of Population I, embedded in dust, pervaded by and enclosed in a spherical or spheroidal haze of Population II stars and globular clusters.

We have seen pure Population II systems, with populations like those of globular clusters, in the dwarf companions of Messier 31 — *elliptical galaxies*. And we have surveyed pure Population I systems, companions of our own galaxy — *irregular galaxies*.

The results of a census of galaxies show that these forms are typical; there are others of intermediate or anomalous character, but these provide a skeleton classification of galaxies. The elliptical systems, the faint dwarf galaxies, seem to be the vast majority. The spirals are a poor second in point of numbers, and the irregular galaxies apparently the rarest of all. Like the varieties of stars, the complex of galaxies is found in all types of physical association: spirals with ellipticals, spirals with irregulars, pairs of spirals, pairs of ellipticals . . . the variety is endless. Can the galaxies be fitted into a coherent scheme of development? Will that scheme place the component stars in a reasonable sequence? These will be the themes of a later chapter.

THE DRAMA

THE DRAMA

6   The Ages of Things

We approach the reconstruction of the cosmic drama. We have met the players: stars, atoms, and dust. The associations between players have passed in review; we have seen intimate relations between pairs of stars, and within stellar families, great and small. We have surveyed the panoramas of the whole stage, witnessed the actors in a variety of groups.

Before we can reconstruct the course of the drama, we must set the stage. We need to know how things began. What was the original stage setting, and how has the plot developed from these beginnings? The question of how things began is wrapped up with the equally important question: when? How old are the actors? How long ago did they first take their places in the situations that we have surveyed?

In thinking of cosmic ages, we shall find two ideas closely interwoven: those of *age* and of *life expectancy*. The two are evidently quite different, and yet they are closely connected. If we are speaking of creatures of any one kind, such as human beings, the greater the age, the smaller will be the life expectancy: the two add up to the average lifetime. But a human being two days old is a very young human being, and a mosquito two days old may be a very old mosquito. The lifetimes, ages, and life expectancies of living things may be expressed in days, or months, or years, but we cannot say whether a creature two days old is really "old" or "young" unless we know the kind of creature, and its normal life span. The same is true within the wider ambit of the cosmos. An atom ten million years old may be a very young atom; but ten million years may be the whole lifetime of a star.

There is a fundamental way of deciding the ages, life expectancies and life spans of the actors in our drama: we must decide what causes them to age, and find some measure of the speed of the aging process. To put it crudely: how fast are they going to pieces? Stars, as we learned in the first chapter, are gradually consuming their substance. Double stars are drawn apart by the general attraction of the stellar system. Cluster stars are subject to the same disturbing forces, and to the differential motion of the galaxy in which they lie. Galaxies tear their substance to pieces as they spin.

Ages of Atoms. — We cannot think of the universe as we know it without thinking first of atoms, and all plausible ideas of cosmic evolution start out with atoms — atoms such as we know today, and in about the same proportions. One of the most amazing facts about the chemical composition of things is that the proportions of atoms of different kinds seem to be very nearly the same in all stars, in interstellar material that presumably has never been stellar, and in interstellar matter that has been thrown off by stars that have grown so old that they are approaching bankruptcy. In other words, *stars have changed appreciably while the chemical composition of the universe has changed relatively little.* All the stars are gradually using up their hydrogen and changing it into helium, by a process that seems to be inexorably one-way. And yet the vast majority of all cosmic atoms are still atoms of hydrogen. In terms of its life expectancy, the atomic population of the universe is still very young.

How old, in years, are the atoms that populate the universe? We can make an estimate by seeing how fast they are going to pieces. Like star clusters and stars, some atoms disintegrate, and the rate of the process can be accurately measured. I do not refer to the outer haze of electrons that is responsible for the chemical and physical properties of the atoms, and for the nature of the light absorbed or emitted. These are only the outer garments of the atom. The disintegration is more deep-seated. The cores, the *nuclei* of atoms, seem to be built up from still more fundamental entities, protons and neutrons. The properties of these basic ingredients of matter are starkly elusive, and the forces that bind them together are of a different sort from the interactions of stars and planets.

Most nuclei are extremely *stable*: they are capable of enduring indefinitely without change. But some are inherently unstable, have a tendency to go to pieces under everyday conditions. If, in some way, one member of a cluster of basic particles acquires enough energy to overcome the attraction of the rest, it will fly off and be lost — and the atomic nucleus will have undergone disintegration. The process has become familiar under the name of *radioactivity*. Most of the very heavy atomic nuclei have this sort of instability, but the effect is not peculiar to heavy nuclei.

An atomic nucleus of a particular kind has a definite tendency to instability — a definite life expectancy. If a crowd of unstable atoms of one kind is watched for a given interval (say a year), *the same fraction of them will always be seen to go to pieces*. One can picture the process by a human analogy. Over the Labor Day weekend, for example, the authorities are able to predict with great accuracy how many people will perish in automobile accidents, though of course they cannot state *which* individuals will be killed. A similar rule governs the prediction of nuclear fatalities. The same fraction will always occur within a given time to any one kind of unstable atom. To determine what that fraction is, it is only necessary, so to speak, to count the atomic corpses. That is exactly what the physicist does. Some atoms, like that of ordinary carbon, are practically accident-free; for some others, half the population perishes within a fraction of a second.

The tendency to this type of nuclear fatality is often expressed, in fact, by stating the time that must elapse before half the nuclei have perished — the *half life*. These half lives can clearly give us an idea of the age of the atomic population of the universe. For example, if an atom has a very short half life, we shall expect to find no survivors of this kind from the primitive population.

Such atoms have recently been in the public eye: plutonium and neptunium are examples of them. They were used (just because of their tendency to go to pieces, with results fatal to mankind) in the construction of "atomic" bombs. But we had to *make* them (by subjecting other atoms to certain conditions into which I shall not go); they are not found in nature.

There are several kinds of plutonium. The least accident-prone variety has a half life of about twenty thousand years. We know that atoms of plutonium can be formed, for we have done it. There were probably atoms of plutonium in the primitive universe. But because there are none left in the atomic population today, we must suppose that they have virtually all perished. In other words, the atomic population is much more than twenty thousand years old. The least accident-prone kind of neptunium has a half life of 20 million years; as neptunium is not found in nature, we can conclude that the cosmic population of atoms is more than 20 million years old.

The universe, however, does contain natural uranium in small quantities. Uranium, too, disintegrates at a known, steady rate. Its nuclei undergo several successive fatalities, pass through a series of atomic reincarnations as forms of thorium, radium, and bismuth, and end up finally as stable nuclei, a form of *lead*. These atoms of lead are, so to speak, the corpses of the original atoms of uranium, and by counting them we can obtain a measure of how many atoms of uranium have perished. The proneness of the uranium to fatalities has been measured, and from the number of corpses it is easy to calculate how long the accidents have been going on. The result is about 4500 million years. Another corpse left by the way as uranium disintegrates is that of helium, and by measuring the helium that has been produced, we reach the figure of 5500 million years.

Two different kinds of uranium are found in nature, and they go to pieces at different rates. The one that is more accident-prone is, as we might expect, far less common than the other, in a ratio of less than 1 to 100. If we make the rough but plausible guess that in the beginning these two kinds of uranium were equally common, we can calculate how long a time must have elapsed to reduce the proportion of the less fortunate one to less than 1 percent of the other. It is found to be about 6000 million years.

These are tremendous intervals of time, but the three bases of calculation all give about the same result. The information from unstable atoms sets a sort of horizon for the cosmic time scale, of less than 10,000 million years. There was a day (not so very long ago) when astronomers were willing to contemplate an even longer interval, about a thousand times as great. But there is a general feeling nowadays, as we shall see, that all our information about the ages of stars and stellar systems seems to fit within the shorter framework of a few thousand million years — the "short time scale" of a generation ago, but still long enough, in all conscience!

Most conservative astronomers are unwilling to say more than that an interval of about 10,000 million years in the past has seen appreciable changes in the universe. To attempt to say what happened before that, what gave birth to the atoms themselves, is both difficult and dangerous.

One thing is certain: the conditions requisite for the building of atomic nuclei are very different from anything that we observe in interstellar space, or on the stars, or even from anything that we suppose to be happening within the stars today. This is one of the difficulties that face the proponents of the idea that atoms are being born into the universe continuously: the necessary conditions seem to be lacking.

Two ways of picturing the birth of atoms have been suggested. One idea depicts their birth by the "cookery" of their ultimate constituents at fantastic temperatures, between a million million degrees and a hundred million million degrees, in a mass that later cooled to the relatively moderate temperatures (tens of millions of degrees at most) that prevail today. Even so, it seems necessary, in order to account for the observed numbers of atoms of different kinds, to suppose that the cookery took place in two stages; no one temperature will do the job.

Another idea imagines that all the material in the universe was once concentrated in a sort of vast superatom, which went to pieces (by a sort of nuclear fission, such as occurs on a very modest (!) scale in the "atomic" bomb) into the kinds of atoms that populate the present universe. This second idea, which sees the origin of the cosmos as we know it in a gigantic explosion, finds some support in the fact that the stellar systems that fill the observable scene do appear to be expanding, or exploding, in all directions away from us. But this observed fact can also be looked at in another way, as we shall see.

Most of us feel safest if we confine ourselves to two statements: the atoms are there; and they are probably older than the stars. Only a small fraction of the hydrogen in the universe has at present been converted into helium. The life expectancy of the stars is tied up with the life expectancy of their hydrogen population. The other stable atoms have, indeed, an indefinite future, and the ultimate state of the atomic population will probably be an assemblage of atoms of helium, with a slight contamination of heavier elements. But the time when this stage will be reached is far beyond our future horizon.

Age of the Earth. — Before we consider the evidence on the ages and life expectancies of stars, let us give a side glance at the age of the part of the universe that most concerns us — the earth on which we live. The problem of the age of the earth is in the province of geology. All methods of estimating it point to a very long interval. Mammals have existed on earth for perhaps 50 million years; reptiles go back perhaps twice as far; there is evidence for life of some kind 500 million years back; and the crust of the earth is estimated, by radioactive methods, to be about 3000 million years old. For contrast, we may remember that man goes back a hundred thousand years or so, recorded history about seven thousand years, and a civilization that lasts a couple of millenia is doing every well indeed.

These figures for the age of the earth reveal a remarkable thing. The evidence of the atoms suggests an age of about 5000 million years; the earth seems to be nearly as old. This strikes at the root of the simple cosmogonic picture that imagined that the atoms came first, then the stars, and then the planets, born from the stars. There does not seem to be enough time left for all this to happen. What do we know about the age of the sun itself?

Age of the Sun. — The age of the sun was the vexed question of the last years of the nineteenth century. We can be fairly certain that the amount of light received by the earth from the sun has not changed very much since life existed on our planet. If the sun sent us only 10 percent less light and heat, the earth would be too cold for living things; if it sent us 10 percent more, water would boil at the surface of our planet, and life would be impossible. The continuous existence of life on earth, as revealed in the fossil record, shows that the sun has not only been there, but has been essentially the same as now, for at least 500 million years, a tenth of the interval since the time horizon! The sun lies near the middle of the orderly main sequence of stars. It is not likely to have changed rapidly or radically, even before this quiescent interval began.

The earth is not now thought to have been produced catastrophically by disruption of the sun. More probably, sun and earth originated as part of the same process: the earth was never part of the sun, and perhaps it was never even at a very high temperature, but came directly from solid material that condensed to form both sun and planets. The sun (as we know it) may indeed be younger than the earth, not older.

Ages of Stars. — The problem of the ages of the stars is closely interwoven with the problem of stellar nutrition. The stars must be subsisting on the nuclear energy of their own atoms; no other adequate source can be imagined for the energy they radiate. The two processes that probably feed the stars were described in an earlier chapter: the carbon cycle and the proton-proton reaction. The details are different, but the main feature is the same. Hydrogen nuclei are the food of the stars, and by one route or another they are converted into nuclei of helium.

A star can shine only so long as hydrogen is available, and it can last only so long as it husbands its supply. The vast majority of all atoms in the universe are atoms of hydrogen, and we may surmise that the same is true of the composition of stars at the beginning of their careers. Let us make a crude guess that a star sets out with about half hydrogen by *weight*; this will allow for the fact that hydrogen is the lightest of all atoms. Then its life expectancy will be in direct proportion to its total mass, and in inverse proportion to the rate at which it consumes its food.

We are not sure that a star is able to consume all its hydrogen; indeed most probably only about one tenth of all the hydrogen atoms are available as food, for rather recondite reasons that depend on the mysterious details of stellar structure. Let us then assume that only one twentieth of the total weight of a star can undergo the hydrogen to helium transformation that supplies its light.

We can calculate exactly how much light the process will produce. The hydrogen is not annihilated; it is merely turned into helium by the fusion of four atoms of hydrogen. Now the helium atom weighs a little less (0.7 percent, in fact) than the four atoms of hydrogen that went to make it; the excess mass is turned into energy in accordance with the celebrated Einstein relation (p. 4), and ultimately appears as starlight. The stars shine only because of the slight loss of mass that accompanies the fusion of the four hydrogen nuclei. The Einstein equation allows us to calculate exactly how much light is produced by the consumption of a given amount of hydrogen; and if we know the total brightness of a star, we can determine precisely the cost in hydrogen atoms consumed.

The stellar balance sheet can be presented in a tabulation (Table 1). Most of the stars for which we can state the assets and liabilities are double stars, for these alone, as will be recalled, can be weighed. We first determine the assets: the star's total mass, the mass that is available for nutrition (one twentieth of the total), and the total mass of the light that can be given out (seven thousandths of the available mass). On the other side we can line up the star's liabilities: the mass equivalent of the light that it is expending per second. A very simple division will tell us the length of time that the star can survive at the present rate of expenditure.

Let us emphasize that the tabular entries have a fallacious precision. Many assumptions have gone into the calculations. Suppose, for example, that the interior of the star is kept well stirred (perhaps because the star is rotating); then it may have access to the whole of its available hydrogen, not just a tenth of it. Such a star would have ten times the life expectancy that is given in the table. A star that set out with over 50 percent of hydrogen by weight would likewise have a greater lease of life. The stellar balance sheet can be drawn up only approximately; the entires in the last two columns are known within a factor of ten.

The assets and liabilities of the stars are necessarily given in enormous units. The masses of stars and their available radiation are in units of 1 million million million million (or 10^{24}) tons. Expenditure of light is given in millions of tons per second. The unit chosen for stellar life expectancies is 1 billion (10^9) years.

TABLE 1. STELLAR BALANCE SHEET.

Name of Star	Mass (10^{24} tons*)	Mass Equivalent of Possible Radiation (10^{24} tons*)	Rate of Expenditure of Light (10^6 tons* per second)	Life Expectancy (10^9 years)	Life Expectancy (compared to that of our Sun)
Main Sequence					
Krüger 60A **	535	0.19	0.02	398	76
Krüger 60B	357	0.12	0.006	658	125
μ Herculis A	(1983)	0.69	13.7	1.6	0.3
μ Herculis B	990	0.35	0.12	9.1	1.7
μ Herculis C	795	0.28	0.08	11.1	2.1
η Cassiopeiae A	1590	0.56	3.82	4.6	0.9
η Cassiopeiae B	1190	0.42	0.14	97	18.5
70 Ophiuchi A	1780	0.62	2.11	9.3	1.8
70 Ophiuchi B	1590	0.56	0.93	19.0	3.6
a Centauri A	2180	0.76	5.06	4.8	0.9
a Centauri B	1870	0.65	2.91	7.1	1.3
ζ Herculis A	2180	0.76	20.20	1.2	0.2
ζ Herculis B	990	0.35	0.84	12.7	2.4
Our Sun	1983	0.69	4.21	5.25	1.0
σ Coronae A	3370	1.18	8.02	4.6	0.9
Borealis B	1590	0.56	3.50	5.0	1.0
Procyon	2180	0.76	23.6	1.0	0.2
Sirius	4850	1.70	216	0.24	0.04
Giants					
Capella A	8350	3.02	5550	0.02	0.003
Capella B	6550	2.29	3590	0.02	0.003
Arcturus	23800	8.33	5300	0.05	0.01
Aldebaran	(7950)	2.78	14000	0.006	0.001
β Pegasi	(17800)	6.23	30600	0.006	0.001
Supergiants					
Betelgeuse	(29800)	10.43	40200	0.008	0.002
Antares	(59600)	20.86	112000	0.006	0.001
Rigel	(65000)	22.75	86000	0.008	0.002
UW Canis Majoris	71500	25.03	26700000	0.00003	0.000006

* Metric tons are used; 1 metric ton = 2205 lb. Masses given in parentheses are estimates based on the mass-luminosity law.

** In a double or multiple star, the components are distinguished by the letters A, B, etc.

The stellar masses given in parentheses are mere estimates, made on the assumption that the stars conform to the mass-luminosity law. But that is not certain for all stars. A large and important group, the subgiants, are *overluminous*, more luminous than the "law" would suggest; they are more prodigal than main-sequence stars of similar mass, and their life expectancies are proportionately less.

The mass of Arcturus is not directly measured, for Arcturus is not a double star with a known orbit; its mass is inferred from its spectral peculiarities. Arcturus seems to have an abnormal mass for its brightness: it is *underluminous* (it radiates less light than we should expect for a star of its mass). The abnormality is probably real and significant, for Arcturus is one of the few high-velocity stars that are nearby and therefore can be scanned in detail. Perhaps Population II in general is marked by a similar parsimony of radiation, and its notorious lack of supergiant stars of high luminosity may thus receive an interpretation. Few masses are known for stars of Population II, because double stars, though not unknown there, are rarer than in Population I.

Though the precise values of life expectancy are unknown, the main tenor of the table is quite definite. The sun, and most of the main-sequence stars, have a life expectancy that is comparable to or greater than the 5000 million years that was set by the atoms for the distance to the time-horizon of the past. Only when we reach Sirius on the main sequence do we find life expectancies less than 1000 million years.

With the giant stars it is another story altogether, from Capella with 20 million years ahead to β Pegasi with only 6 million; and the most luminous supergiant in the table, the great eclipsing system UW Canis Majoris, gives the amazing result of a mere three hundred thousand years. The life expectancy for the brightest known star, S Doradus in the Large Magellanic Cloud, is even smaller.

The results of this table are staggering; but it is difficult to gainsay them. They state that the duration of life on earth has been greater than the possible lifetimes of the most luminous stars. If Rigel was shining at the time (200 million years ago) when the coal measures were laid down, it would have used up its hydrogen by now. But Rigel is still shining; we can only conclude that it began to shine long since life walked our earth. If S Doradus were shining half a million years ago, it could not be there now — at least not in its present splendor. Rigel and S Doradus must be infant stars, in comparison to which the earth is an old-timer.

The sun, on the other hand, has a possible lifetime not very different from, and perhaps as much as, ten times the interval since the time horizon set by the atoms. We can conclude that the solar energy is far from being exhausted; probably we can count on our luminary for a long time to come (though whether we can count on his remaining unchanged throughout his life is another question). Precise calculations by Ledoux suggest that the sun has in fact consumed just about half its available hydrogen.

The table tells the total possible lifetime of the stars of various kinds. Their life expectancies, of course, depend on how long they have been shining already. If their total life is over 5000 million years, we cannot tell for how much of this interval they have lived.

There is a possible way of estimating even this, though it is beset with pitfalls. If we can make an estimate of how large a fraction of its hydrogen a star has consumed, we can guess how far it has gone on its way. Counts of hydrogen atoms in the atmospheres of stars are rather treacherous; but there is a suggestion that the Population II stars do have less than the Population I stars of similar brightness. If we read this clue aright, it means that the Population II stars have been going longer — they are older in years than the superficially similar Population I stars.

The conception of age is highlighted by the table. In the same number of years that would carry Rigel from youth to decrepitude, from prodigality to bankruptcy, a star like the sun would scarcely age at all. We saw a similar difference among atoms; an assemblage of atoms of neptunium perishes in an interval that sees less change in a group of uranium atoms, and no change at all in a group of ordinary atoms of, say, carbon. We shall see it again among star clusters and galaxies; their aging process cannot be measured in years alone.

One fundamental assumption made in calculating the possible stellar lifetimes should be especially emphasized. The figures were obtained on the assumption that the stars in question have always radiated at the same rate. In other words, they imply that a star of a given mass always has the same luminosity — the mass-luminosity relation. Even if a star were made entirely of hydrogen, and converted it all into helium, the loss of mass would only be 0.7 percent of the whole — a quite negligible quantity. Therefore, if the total masses of stars are altered only by loss from radiation, stars maintain essentially the same mass all their lives. Therefore, if the mass-luminosity law is valid throughout the stellar lifetime, our assumption is a justifiable one.

There are, however, large deviations from the mass-luminosity law. Struve has pointed out that the components of eclipsing stars, notably the "Algol stars," are the most flagrant examples: the fainter, larger companion tends to be *overluminous*. The same, as Struve has also shown, is true to a lesser extent for one of the components of the dwarf twin systems (twins in brightness, *but not in mass!*) that are very close together, short in period, and tidally distorted — the so-called W Ursae Majoris stars. On the other hand, as we have seen, the stars of Population II may possibly be *underluminous*. The overluminous stars will have shorter lifetimes than would be predicted from adherence to the mass-luminosity law; the underluminous stars can protract their existence. Some of the consequences of these possibilities will concern us in the last chapter.

The most underluminous stars of all are the white dwarfs, which radiate a hundred or even a thousand times less than the mass-luminosity law would lead us to expect. These stellar bankrupts, as we have seen, have probably exhausted virtually all their hydrogen capital. Are we to infer enormous ages for them? If the sun goes back to the time horizon, what of Sirius B, the "Pup," of almost equal mass? Is it much older than the sun? How then does it happen to be teamed up with a comparatively youthful star? This question will be discussed, if not answered, in the final chapter.

Ages of Double Stars. — In the third chapter we surveyed the double stars; the stellar twins that were born together and have lived their lives in company. Stellar unions, I said, are virtually indissoluble; but with the passage of time the pair tends to draw gradually apart under the attraction of the other stars.

The rate at which external influences will separate close stellar companions can be calculated. On the average, as was shown by Ambartsumian, it will take about 10,000 million years to draw a pair apart to the distance of ten thousand times the distance of the earth from the sun. Many visual binaries are within this limit; and, as we have seen, the great majority of all stars (probably more than half) are members of binary sytems. The inference is that the disturbing influence of the stellar system has been acting for not longer than 10,000 million years. The interval is suspiciously near the one that we derived from atomic fatalities for the past age of the atomic population.

Ages of Star Clusters. — Clusters of stars are not merely examples of huge stellar families built up on the same pattern as the whole complex family of double stars. They, too, will give us an idea of their ages from the study of how fast they are going to pieces. The attraction of the whole stellar system tends to pull stars out of the cluster, and the attraction of the whole cluster tends to keep them in it. We need not go into technicalities to convince ourselves that the heavier, denser clusters will hold together better than the loose ones that contain few stars. The cluster in Ursa Major, which contains most of the stars of the Big Dipper, is not dense enough or massive enough to hold together very well; it is going to pieces before our eyes and has a life expectancy of perhaps 200 million years. The Pleiades, both denser and more massive, with a weight equal to about four hundred suns, may live, as Bok has shown, from first to last about 3000 million years — not far from the distance to the early time horizon — and may end by collapse rather than by disintegration. We can hardly suppose that these clusters are older than the atoms, but they may perhaps be much younger — possibly very much younger. A loose, light cluster that is beginning to go to pieces is likely to be older than a cluster of comparable population that is still compact. We notice with interest that the galactic clusters that are loosest contain, on the whole, fewer bright stars and fewer hot ones. In the same way, the close double stars, which we discover as spectroscopic binaries, include all the luminous ones of high temperature (as well as a great number of cooler, fainter ones); the widely separated double stars, seen as visual doubles, are never among the very luminous ones at high temperatures. We begin to see a thread of development: the clusters and the double stars that are closely compacted, have drawn apart the least, and are therefore probably the most recently formed, contain the brightest, hottest stars. We shall see the significance of this fact in the last chapter: they are probably the youngest of their kind. The stellar associations that we met in Chapter 4 must (if they are real physical systems) be at most a few million years old.

The globular clusters move in paths highly inclined to the Milky Way. They are far denser, far more massive than the galactic clusters, and are in small danger of disruption under the influence of the galactic system. They are so massive that their own attraction will keep their members under control for an indefinite time. And they are free from another influence that is a potent disintegrator of galactic clusters: they are not subject to the disrupting effects of the differential rotation of the thin layer where the galactic clusters move, within the central haze of dust and atoms. Clusters so compact and populous would be little affected by the distortion of the rotating galaxy. Globular clusters have an enormous life expectancy, and may well be of enormous age.

Ages of Galaxies. — What of the ages of the galaxies themselves? The elliptical galaxies, which resemble globular clusters on a huge scale, have a similar future and probably a similar history. Their life expectancy is practically indefinite, and they, too, may be of enormous age.

Spiral galaxies tell a very different story. They are spinning, and spinning nonuniformly. At the center they move more slowly than farther out, and in their outermost regions again they move more slowly. In other words, they do not rotate like wheels. But if they are to maintain their present shape, their rotation must be wheellike. Any change of the angular speed of rotation along a spoke would distort a wheel. And we know that the speed of rotation varies in galaxies along their imaginary spokes. So their shapes, and the forms of the spiral arms, must be steadily twisting into new forms. We can calculate that a galaxy that started out with spiral arms like those of Messier 33 (Plate 53) would, within a few thousand million years, be wound up as tightly as a ball of twine. But we do not find spirals that are wound up tightly. Most of the arms show only one or two complete turns; many display less than one. The inference is inescapable: the arms that we see today cannot be old; they would be quite torn out of existence in ten to a hundred million years.

Are the galaxies, then, so much younger than stars like the sun, which must be thousands of millions of years old? Here we touch the core of the problem. The conspicuous features of the galaxies, their spiral arms, must be young; and notice that they are about the same age as the spendthrift stars. But it is only these spendthrift stars that reveal the spiral arms — the hot, luminous stars, and star clusters, the nebulosity that they excite, the Cepheid variables. We begin to see the spiral arms as evanescent structures, marked out by groups of young stars that lie within the layer of dust and gas, with lifetimes from a tenth to a hundreth of the interval since the early time horizon.

But, as we saw in the last chapter, the spiral arms are only a small part of the galaxies that display them; they comprise 1 to 10 percent of all the stars in the whole system, and probably about 1 percent of its mass; notice that the ratio 100 occurs in the numbers, as it did in the ages. Here again, as with the stars and the galaxies, the conspicuous is not the most important; faint stars outnumber the bright stars that strike the eye; faint galaxies outnumber the bright galaxies; spiral arms obtrude themselves on our attention, but they are not the whole cake; they are only the rare and evanescent features of the central filling. The stars of the surrounding haze may be very old indeed.

What, then, of the irregular galaxies, the objects like the Magellanic Clouds? I shall speak of them in the next chapter, which deals with the development of stellar systems. They show little or no spiral structure and seem to be populated largely by spendthrifts. My own belief is that these are systems that are as young as the spiral arms of galaxies. The Large Cloud seems to show rudiments of spirality, the Small Cloud none at all; either it has had no time to develop spiral structure, or is not capable of doing so. Certainly the Clouds seem to bear none of the marks of antiquity. Perhaps they are spendthrift galaxies, comparable to the individual supergiant stars; the Magellanic Clouds are the Rigels among the stellar systems. On the other hand, the elliptical galaxies are more of the nature of bankrupt galaxies, and comparable to the white dwarfs among the stars. Irregular galaxies, like Rigels, are uncommon; like the white dwarfs the elliptical galaxies are very common indeed. But the analogy is only an analogy, and should not be pressed too far. Elliptical galaxies do not *consist* of bankrupt stars (though they may contain many, inaccessible to observation because of their remoteness); but they are bankrupt in the sense that their capacity to produce new stars has been exhausted. They have no dust and gas from which stars can be born.

Ages of Clusters of Galaxies. — The greatest of all the groupings of objects in the universe are the clusters of galaxies. We have seen small groups of galaxies: Messier 31 and its elliptical companions; our own galaxy and its Magellanic Clouds; Messier 81 and its companions — these are the analogues of double and multiple stars. But there are great clusters, groups of several hundred galaxies, that correspond to the galactic clusters. These, like the galactic clusters, can provide one more test of the ages of things. The motions of their members can be measured, and the interval during which they can be expected to hold together can be calculated. Some of the largest can be shown to have a life expectancy of about 10,000 million years. The fact that we observe many of these great clusters of galaxies — and their known number is being augmented all the time — shows that they fit within the frame of the time horizon that was given by the atoms.

Another argument is often used to estimate the age of the system of the galaxies. When their speeds are measured with the spectroscope, all the galaxies appear to be receding from us, and the most distant ones seem to be going the fastest. This observation — the apparent recession of the galaxies, often interpreted as an expansion of the universe — can be naïvely regarded as evidence of a true explosion. But such a view introduces great difficulties: it leads to a figure of only 1000 million years since the expansion started — less than the interval allowed by atoms, or stars, or even the age of the earth itself! A more sophisticated view takes into account the difficult concepts of the theory of relativity, which ascribes some of the apparent recession to the curved nature of space. This view leads us to expect delicate changes in the observed numbers and colors of galaxies with distance, at about the limit that can be reached with the 200-inch telescope, and the data are still being collected. At present the observed recession of the galaxies is compatible with a wide range of time scales, and certainly cannot be used to date the beginning of the expansion, without making assumptions that are not justified by the present state of our knowledge.

If we try to summarize our present ideas about the ages of things, I think we can state that the ages of the earth, of most stars,

TABLE 2. Approximate Cosmic Ages (years).

Ages of Atoms	
Plutonium	over 20,000
Neptunium	over 20,000,000
Uranium: lead ratio	4,500,000,000
Uranium: helium ratio	5,500,000,000
Uranium balance	6,000,000,000
Age of the Earth	
Civilization	2,000
Prehistory	7,000
Man	100,000
Mammals	50,000,000
Reptiles	100,000,000
Life	500,000,000
Crust of the earth	3,000,000,000
Life Expectancies of Stars	
Faint dwarfs	600,000,000,000
Sun	over 5,000,000,000
Supergiants	500,000 to 10,000,000
Life Expectancies of Stellar Systems	
Double Stars	less than 10,000,000,000
Star Clusters:	
Ursa Major	200,000,000
Pleiades	3,000,000,000
Globular clusters	over 10,000,000,000
Galaxies:	
Elliptical	over 10,000,000,000
Spiral:	
Arms	10–50,000,000
Nuclei	10,000,000,000
Irregular	400,000,000
Clusters of Galaxies	less than 10,000,000,000

of star clusters, and of clusters of galaxies, fit reasonably well within the framework of time suggested by the age of the atomic population, with a time horizon of several thousand million years (Table 2). Two groups of objects lead to very much smaller ages: the spendthrift stars and the arms of spiral galaxies. As these two phenomena are closely bound up with one another, and the arms of galaxies are made visible and marked out by the stellar spendthrifts, we cannot but conclude that the latter are really young. We can even toy with the idea that stars are being born continuously; and the places where the young stars are found suggest very definitely that they are born of the interstellar dust. Our current ideas about the way in which stars come into being, and the course of their subsequent careers, will be the subjects of our final chapter.

7   The Evolution of Galaxies

Our own galaxy contains perhaps a hundred thousand million stars. But it is only one of many; there are millions, if not hundreds of millions, of accessible galaxies (accessible, that is, to our present telescopes). Our own system has the distinction of being one of the biggest, brightest, and most massive.

As we saw in the last chapter, galaxies differ very much in structure. Some, like the companions to Messier 31, are globular or elliptical — quite structureless and beautifully symmetrical. In fact, they recall the globular clusters (though many of them are much more flattened). However, all of them are so much larger and most of them so much brighter than globular clusters that they must be regarded as a different kind of individual.

Some galaxies are quite irregular in form, ragged complexes of stars, gas, and dust; such are the Magellanic Clouds, our own companions. And some, the most beautiful of all, are spiral. There are many kinds of spirals, from lightly outlined systems with faint central nuclei, through systems with small, well-marked nuclei and sharply defined arms, to systems that seem to be mostly nucleus, with faint arms encircling them.

Our problem is this: can we arrange the galaxies in a continuous series; and if we can do so, which way is the series headed? Which are the young galaxies, which are the old ones?

We spent some time on the family portraits of groups of stars; galaxies have their family patterns too. In sketching the features of the stars we found that brightness, size, and color were among their important properties. I have said nothing so far about the lineaments of galaxies; but here, too, size, brightness, and color are very significant.

Between the most luminous and the faintest galaxies known, there is a ratio of about 200 in total brightness. Our own galaxy is perhaps the brightest known, and the faintest hitherto recognized is one of the small companions of the Andromeda galaxy. An isolated elliptical galaxy in Sculptor may be even a little fainter.

This range of 200 in brightness among galaxies is not nearly as great as the range of brightness among stars, which amounts to millions. But it is large enough to produce on our observations of galaxies the same effect as variety in brightness produces on our observations of stars. Very luminous stars, visible at great distances, obtrude themselves on our attention, and we tend to overestimate their numbers and perhaps to exaggerate their importance. Very bright galaxies, also, are seen more readily than faint ones at great distances, and lead us to exaggerate our ideas of their frequency. We remember that the faint, small stars of small mass are the enormous majority. In the same way, when we make the proper allowance for the modesty of the fainter galaxies, we find that they, too, are in the majority. The *average* galaxy in space has been found to be about one hundredth as bright as our own, and the faint galaxies are so very self-effacing that quite possibly an average galaxy may be even fainter than this.

The sizes of galaxies, too, have a large range, though not as great as their range of brightness. The companions of the galaxy in Andromeda have perhaps a tenth or a twentieth of the extent of the great spiral.

The sizes, luminosities, and structures of galaxies are closely related with one another, and the connection between them is certainly very important. All the spirals are large and bright. Some are not, it is true, as large as our own. The beautiful spiral in Canes Venatici (Plate 42) is perhaps one quarter the size and a couple of magnitudes fainter. But below these limits we do not seem to find many spirals.

The relation between size and brightness for the irregular galaxies is not quite so clean-cut. But on the average they are smaller than the spirals, and many of them are smaller than any spiral ever found.

Elliptical galaxies are even less restricted in size and brightness. The great majority are small and faint — smaller and fainter, indeed, than any other kind of galaxy — but we also observe large, bright ones. Some of them rival the brightest spirals in brightness, if not in size. As we shall see, size and brightness must be taken into account, as well as form and structure, before we can arrange galaxies in a coherent scheme.

I have mentioned that the small, faint galaxies form the great majority. That statement can be refined a little. The commonest galaxies are the small, faint, elliptical systems; next in numbers come the spirals. Among these, the smaller, fainter spirals are commoner than the large, bright ones like our own; but let me repeat that there are no spirals at all below a certain limit of brightness, as Shapley first pointed out. Irregular galaxies are the rarest of all. We hardly know enough to say whether large or small irregular galaxies preponderate; but it is fairly certain that very big ones like the Large Magellanic Cloud are quite rare.

If we are to arrange the complex system of galaxies, with all their variety of structure, size, and brightness, in an orderly series that represents their course of development, we must find some criteria of age and state of evolution on which to base our arrangement. But when we bear in mind the analogy with men and mosquitoes, we shall realize that *age* and *aging* are not necessarily the same. A system that is relatively young in years may be old in development.

There are some very broad principles on which one can evaluate aging among stellar systems. First, and perhaps most important, is orderliness. It seems to be an inexorable law that time smooths out all things, that irregularities tend to disappear with aging, to be replaced by order, homogeneity, and monotony. An aged system seems to lose its enterprise.

There is a deep-seated reason for this. In the last chapter I said that I believe (without, it is true, advancing all the arguments in favor of the belief) that atoms came before stars. From the atoms were built the dust, the stars, and the stellar systems that we know (not necessarily in this order). The stars and galaxies must have originated from clouds of atoms, in other words from masses of *gas*.

Now diffuse gas has some properties that are very different from those of solid matter, or even of gas compressed into stars. Odd as it may sound, gas is sticky; it possesses *viscosity*. Moreover, large, diffuse masses of gas are bound to be swirling and churning; even if they were not doing so to begin with, they would be certain to break up into eddies as time went on. The solid particles that begin to form within the gas, and produce the dust and haze, are caught up in the motions of the swirling gas; they ride the atomic winds, and we see the shredded clouds, for example, in the neighborhood of the Pleaides. The solid particles are not sticky; they are too far apart to affect one another very much. The stars are even more widely separated, and affect one another very little, so that, as I put it earlier, stellar collisions are virtually impossible, and stellar unions are practically indissoluble.

The swirling, churning motions of the underlying gas, and the motions of the interstellar clouds that they carry with them, cause a young system (which contains much of both) to be irregular in form and to lack symmetrical structure. If our idea of the development of cosmic objects from a primitive cloud of gas is at all correct, it follows that systems rich in gas and dust must be young systems, and will moreover be expected to be irregular in form. It is significant that the irregular galaxies *are* rich in dust and gas, richer indeed than systems of any other kind. This fact is the basis of our belief that they must be the most youthful of the stellar systems.

Another fact strengthens this conviction. The irregular systems are particularly rich in stellar spendthrifts, and, as we saw in the last chapter, these spendthrifts must be young stars; they can last only a short time, a fraction of the distance from the early time horizon. We began to associate youthfulness with Population I — the stars that show the family portrait typical of the galactic clusters. And we note with interest that the Magellanic Clouds, the hotbeds of Population I, which are full of stellar spendthrifts bedded in nebulosity, seem to be innocent of any members of Population II. Here we have an indication that Population II, typical of the globular-cluster family, is characteristic of stars that have aged more.

We find a confirmation that this idea is on the right lines when we turn to the galaxies that contain only Population II stars, un-contaminated by spendthrifts, dust, or gas — the elliptical galaxies. They are at the opposite end of the series of galactic forms. They are beautifully symmetrical, utterly monotonous in structure. It is not hard to reach the idea that they have aged to the point where all irregularity has been obliterated, all enterprise has been abandoned. Stars are no longer being born in these galaxies. The reason is not far to seek; the raw materials are absent; dust and gas are lacking. There are no stellar spendthrifts, for the material of which they could have been formed was exhausted long ago — perhaps by mak-ing stars, perhaps in other ways to be mentioned later.

Already we have made considerable progress in arranging our sequence; the irregular galaxies are youthful, the elliptical galaxies have aged. Can we fit the spirals in between, with their complex structure, their intermingling of Populations I and II?

The spirals are the crux of our problem. It will be recalled that members of the two populations are distinguished in our own system not only by their physical features, but also by their positions and motions. Population I, characterized by the bright, hot stars, moves round the galactic rotary within a very thin layer of dust and gas. The stars of this population are perhaps not much more than 1 per-cent of the whole stellar content of the galaxy. The stars of Popula-tion II move in all directions, and in orbits of all shapes and sizes, *through* the central layer, not within it. As a consequence, they are arranged in a very thick system, nearly structureless, and condensed toward the nucleus of our galaxy. The stars of Population II in other galaxies form similar substrata, while the spiral arms, marked by Population I stars, dust, and gas, travel with a rotary motion within the central layer.

A spiral galaxy, in fact, consists of two interpenetrating and con-centric systems: a structureless substratum that contains most of the stars and probably most of the mass, and strongly resembles an el-liptical galaxy; and a system of arms. The arms, as we saw in the last chapter, must be evanescent; and their age is quite comparable with the ages of the stellar spendthrifts that inhabit and define them, and excite the gas layer to luminescence. Save for their graceful form, the arms of a spiral galaxy have a great deal in common with an irregular galaxy. Without stretching the imagination too much we may picture a spiral galaxy as an irregular galaxy rotating within an ellipsoidal galaxy, and swirled into pinwheel form by its rotational motion around the nucleus of the former. We begin to see the spiral structure as something churned out of the layer of dust and gas by the rotation of the system, something that is progressively twisted out of existence by its own differential rotation. So long as dust and gas are present, spiral arms will form, and dissipate, and new spiral arms will re-form. The process will go on while there is dust and gas present; when all the raw material is used up, there will be no more spiral arms. We shall be left with a system that will soon be nothing but substratum; it will be indistinguishable from an elliptical galaxy — in fact it will *be* an elliptical galaxy.

We have made another step forward. We have fitted the spiral galaxies in between the irregular and the elliptical galaxies. But is our problem completely solved? I think not. We have still to account for an enormous variety of spirals that range from large to moderate in size, and from forms with a scarcely visible nucleus to forms that are mostly nucleus. We have also to recall that spirals may be associated, as the galaxy in Andromeda is, with elliptical galaxies that are probably of the same age. And then we must remember our own galaxy, accompanied by the Magellanic Clouds — are they the same age as our system? The grouping of spirals with both very old and very young galaxies seems inconsistent.

In considering this thorny problem we must distinguish carefully between age and aging. Perhaps the speed of development depends on something besides the age in years. To decide about this question we must scrutinize the process of development a little more closely.

One of the first clues to the details of the process lies in a statement that I made at the beginning of the chapter. Stars and gas have quite different properties. Gas is sticky; it forms swirls and eddies. But stars affect one another very little. A star that starts out in a certain path may be counted on to pursue that path, or something very close to it, indefinitely. Double stars hang together. Clusters of stars travel through space together, and only the poorest and loosest clusters have dissipated very much since their birth. I have insisted that they must have originated together and have been traveling together ever since. This idea leads us naturally to the conception that the motion of a group of stars reveals the motion of the material from which it was built. An associated group of stars has the same motion as the dust and gas that gave it birth.

Look for a moment at Population II in the galaxy. Its most eminent numbers are the globular clusters, with almost spherical distribution and motion in elliptical, highly inclined orbits. The RR Lyrae stars, perhaps a hundred thousand of them, have very similar distributions and motions. We can but conclude that these distributions and motions tell what was the distribution and motion of the gas from which the stars of Population II were born. We can envisage an almost spherical mass of primitive gas and dust, greatly concentrated to the galactic center.

Other kinds of stars, such as the long-period variables, are distributed in systems that are rather more flattened and have motions that are less extreme. Probably they originated from a mass of gas and dust that was less spherical, but still extended very far upward from the central plane of the galaxy. The Population I stars of today are confined to a very thin plane indeed, perhaps 5 percent of the original thickness. In fact, the galaxy may be pictured as a complex of a number of concentric subsystems that are flattened to different degrees, an idea first expressed by the Swedish astronomer Lindblad.

What conclusion is to be drawn from the variety of distributions and motions? I think we can picture the past development of a spiral galaxy in a very general way, though the basic theory is still, frankly, of the vaguest kind. If a mass of gas, originally spherical, begins to rotate, the gas will probably sink steadily toward the central plane. I do not think that the rate of sinking has been accurately calculated, but I suspect that for a system the size of the galaxy it would be about a thousand million years. Thus we can suppose that the more spherical is the group in which a particular kind of star is arranged, and the more inclined its motions to the central plane, the earlier was it formed in the history of the system. We can picture a galaxy gradually building up its Population II substratum within the steadily sinking mass of dust and gas. The more spherical a subsystem, the older can we suppose it to be (Plate 62).

It can be shown, with great plausibility, that the rate of such process of development must depend on the size and the mass of the galaxy concerned. For a small, light galaxy it will go faster than for a large, massive galaxy. Here we see the sharp distinction between age and aging. At a given age in years, a large, massive galaxy will have aged less than a small, light one. Our own galaxy must age very slowly, for it is one of the largest as galaxies go. On the other hand, a large, massive galaxy starts out with more available material than a smaller one; therefore it can be expected to continue to form stars and to display spiral structure longer.

Here, however, we touch upon a problem that is still unsolved. We do not know exactly what decides the rate at which the gaseous substratum is converted into stars. Its density, its state of motion (eddies and swirls), its temperature, all must be involved. The last factor will to some extent depend on the presence of nearby stars (especially bright and hot ones). Therefore, if it is true that the bright, hot stars are indeed the young ones, the very formation of such stars may temporarily inhibit the formation of more stars in their neighborhood, and further star building may have to wait on the extinction of the spendthrifts. Perhaps this factor, and possibly others that we have not thought of, restrains the promiscuous formation of stars from the dust and gas, and conserves the raw materials. Obviously they have been conserved; in our own system there seems still to be about as much interstellar matter in the central sandwich as there is material in the form of stars. And although we know that stars spill off gases from their surfaces, there is no indication that the rate of spilling is anything like enough to maintain as much interstellar material as this.

We are now in a position to make a guess as to the stages through which a galaxy passes. In its initial stages it is an irregular galaxy, but it is bound to have some tendency to rotate, and rotation will in time begin to produce spiral arms. The shape of the Large Magellanic Cloud gives just a suggestion that it is becoming a spiral (compare Plates 46, 60, and 61). Like many other spirals it has a central bar, dense with stars and full of dust and gas, and from the ends of the bar spring what looks like the beginning of spiral arms. Certainly most of the mass of the Large Cloud is in the bar, and probably the bar contains enough gas to be quite viscous, so that it is turning almost like the spoke of a wheel. The stars within it may have been born so recently that they have had little time to leave their original positions; they still lie within the clouds that gave them birth.

There are two main types of spirals, and the Magellanic Cloud seems to be an embryonic *barred spiral*. All barred spirals have a central bar from the ends of which spring a pair of spiral arms. Probably all barred spirals have a considerable concentration of interstellar material in the bar.

The Andromeda galaxy (Plate 39) and the great spiral Messier 33 in Triangulum (Plate 53) are examples of the other type of spiral, the *normal spiral*. Here, on the picture we have sketched, we should expect the first stage of development to involve only vaguely defined arms and not much of a nucleus. But as development proceeds, the nucleus would grow in size and prominence, as more and more stars were born from the gaseous cloud that was sinking toward the central plane. Probably in early times, when star-building material was common, there would be a large proportion of stars in the arms, and they would illuminate the interstellar gas very brightly. A galaxy in this stage would be like Messier 33. As development went on (see Plates 53 to 62), supplies would grow less rich, fewer stars would adorn the arms, and bright nebulae would not be so conspicuous. The galaxy in Andromeda and our own galaxy may be in such a stage. Finally all the material would be gone, and nothing would remain except the substratum; the spendthrift stars would run their brief course, and only an elliptical galaxy would finally remain.

The total age of our galaxy must be at least as great as that of the sun, which is fixed (at a lower limit) by the age of the earth. Our galaxy seems indeed to go back about to the early time horizon, perhaps 5000 million years ago. Smaller spiral galaxies that have reached the same stage must be younger in years. Perhaps it is significant that spiral galaxies are rare among galaxies in general, and that small spirals are unknown. A small spiral of the age of our own would by now have run its course — as such. The small elliptical galaxies may have been small spirals once, but their careers are over and they are bankrupt of star-building material, or very nearly.

127

One of the small companions of Messier 31 still has a very little, and it is fascinating to note that within the dark streak that crosses this elliptical galaxy there are a few "young" stars, though the rest of the system consists of typical Population II stars.

Can we conclude that all galaxies are the same age, and that the present distribution among the types is a consequence of different rates of aging? I think not. An egregious example is right at our door in the shape of the Magellanic Clouds. If what I have said is true, and the irregular galaxies are the youngest, how is it that two youthful systems are teamed up with our own galaxy, which seems to be about as old as the stellar universe? There is only one possible answer. These two systems are not as old as the galaxy. They may well be less than a hundred millions years old. They do not even both seem to be of quite the same age; the Large Cloud is thick with interstellar material, but the Small Cloud is practically transparent, and therefore contains very little. This would make the Large Cloud even younger than the Small Cloud, and the latter is not old, since it contains neither RR Lyrae stars nor globular clusters, typical of Population II. I think we must conclude that the Magellanic Clouds are really much younger than our galaxy, and were formed out of dust and gas at a comparatively late epoch in the life of the latter.

Old as the galaxy is, it still has a future before it; it still contains the makings of a good many stars, and the possibility of forming some future spiral arms. But the end will come at last, and I think we can find some other galaxies that reveal what our own will look like then. The gigantic elliptical galaxy Messier 87 is about as luminous as our total Population II population; and like our own system it is surrounded with a great haze of globular clusters, just resolved with the 200-inch telescope (Plate 52). In Messier 87 we are perhaps looking at a system even older than our own, and can foresee in it our own future. It may be slightly smaller and fainter than I have suggested, and therefore may have aged a little faster than our own galaxy, so that its age in years may be no greater.

Even Messier 87 has not developed beyond all enterprise; a gigantic jet (invisible in Plate 52 against the brilliant center) seems to be spurting radially outward from its nuclear region.

I have outlined the scheme of development of a galaxy from an irregular system, through spiral forms, to the final stage of an elliptical galaxy. The great majority of systems can be fitted into the scheme, but there are odd ones that do not conform. We also find strange bedfellows, such as we found among stars — for example, elliptical and spiral systems in close association. If what we have just said about the dependence of aging on size is true, we should expect that of two galaxies that started out together, the smaller and the less massive would arrive at the elliptical stage before the other. Messier 31 and its companions are related about as we should expect. But such a pair as Messier 60 (elliptical) and the fainter, spiral N.G.C. 4647, if they are really associated in space, are in the wrong order, for Messier 60 is far the brighter of the two. Our own galaxy and the Magellanic Clouds are even more flagrant. Can anything that happens to galaxies affect their development?

The most fascinating example of what looks like arrested development among stellar systems is found in some of the great, dense clusters of galaxies, such as the one that lies comparatively near to us, seen through the constellation Coma, and called the "Coma cluster" (Plate 67). It contains about eight hundred galaxies, some of them round, some of them spindle-shaped and therefore probably greatly flattened. But the striking thing about them is that none show spiral structure, even though such structure, and especially the central dust sandwich, would be expected in the elongated ones. They seem all to be Population II systems. Where are the spirals and what has happened to the dust within the systems?

The answer to this question, when it was given by Spitzer and Baade, was almost as spectacular as the observations. The Coma galaxies form a dense cluster, so dense that they must be suffering frequent collisions (frequent cosmically speaking, that is). Since the time horizon each one must have collided, on the average, with twenty other galaxies. This is an inevitable result, deduced from the compactness of the cluster and the observed motions of the galaxies within it; there is nothing speculative about it.

But where is the evidence of the collisions? The galaxies seem unscathed; they are sharply defined and symmetrically shaped. And a little reflection shows that this is as it should be. Galaxies are exceedingly "open-work." The stars are so far apart that *two galaxies can pass through each other without noticeably disturbing the motions or positions of their stars.*

But with the dust and the gas in the galaxies it is another story. Gas, as we recollect, is sticky, or viscous. If two galaxies collide, the stars move on undisturbed, but the sticky central layers of gas collide, and collide with explosive violence, because the speeds of the galaxies through one another are immense — several hundred miles a second. The impact of gas on gas is so great that the gas clouds must be thrown violently out into space, carrying with them the dust and smoke. The two systems will sweep one another clean of interstellar matter. Twenty collisions per galaxy have probably been enough to purge away all the star-building material in the Coma cluster. The systems have been arrested in their normal course, and we see a group of galaxies that would now be in all stages from spiral to elliptical if they were not so closely crowded. All are frozen into the forms that they had when collisions finished the cleaning job. Is Messier 87 undergoing a final explosive cleansing?

There are other dense clusters of galaxies too, such as the one in Corona Borealis, that have swept themselves clean and are in a state of arrested development. Such a fate seems inevitable for galaxies that have suffered repeated collisions. There are still questions to be answered: what, for example, has happened to the dust and gas? Our authors think that it has probably formed into new systems long since — perhaps long enough since for collisions to have cleaned them out also.

The idea that colliding galaxies may interpenetrate without affecting their stars, but with the effect of cleaning out their interstellar material, is one that has far-reaching implications. How often has Messier 32 passed through the Andromeda galaxy, and with what effects? Have the Magellanic Clouds ever passed through the galactic plane? If they move under its gravitational pull in circular orbits, their periods of rotation would be about as long as we suppose their total life to have been. Were they born, or was the Large Cloud perhaps born, of the dust and gas thrown out in an intergalactic collision? It is a fascinating thought.

I hope that I have succeeded in giving a clear sketch of the possible course of the evolution of galaxies. Some of what I have said would be the opinion of most astronomers; but some of the opinions are my own. The mode of formation of spiral arms that I have advocated, for instance, seems to lead inevitably to arms that trail, at least on the outside of the galaxy. There are eminent astronomers, such as Lindblad, who think otherwise.

But the main course of development, from irregular galaxies, through spirals, to elliptical systems, is, I think, fairly generally accepted. It is true that it reverses the order, assigned by Hubble many years ago, of "early-type" and "late-type" spirals; but the reversed order has long been advocated by Shapley. The general theory of the development of spirals owes much to the brilliant imagination of Carl Friedrich von Weiszäcker, and I own that I have been greatly influenced by his ideas. There are still many problems; first of all we need more observations, and the 200-inch is getting them. Only when enough observations are available shall we be in a position to make new theories. The very basis of the theory of the motions of the interstellar gas is still in its infancy. But I feel a growing vein of confidence that we have at least arranged the systems in the right order, and that we know at least some of the factors most important in their development.

But the subject is so new, so replete with promise and with pitfalls, that only the incurable optimism of the astronomer can excuse the temerity with which I have described it. The evolution of galaxies is still "hot off the griddle"; perhaps a more cautious man would have dismissed it as "too hot to handle."

8   The Evolution of the Stars

The problem of stellar evolution is the most fascinating and the most elusive in astronomy. The stars are spread before us in extraordinary variety, and for many of them our knowledge of the superficial properties, such as brightness, size, surface temperature, mass, and external composition, is fairly complete. We also know a great deal about the relations within groups of stars, and we have learned that within a galaxy both motion and distribution (which are inevitably connected) are intimately linked with other physical properties.

Our task is to knit all these facts into a connected story of the development of stellar character, to infer the changes by which a star proceeds from infancy to old age. And here we run into our greatest stumbling block. The development of stellar character stems from within; the springs of stellar behavior are deep-seated, unobservable. We know, it is true, that the internal conditions of stars are very different from the exterior ones, that the central temperatures and pressures must be very high. But the actual temperatures and pressures depend upon the stars' structure and current composition. We are fairly confident that most stars are subsisting on the energy of their own nuclear substance; a steady change of composition is inevitable, and necessarily brings with it an ultimate change of structure.

The Basic Information. — I have tried in the preceding chapters to summarize the basic facts that seem to me to be the most important leads in our problem. First in order are the observable properties of stars: their variety in brightness, size, and mass; their overwhelming tendency to form doubles, multiple systems, and

132

even larger groups; the close relation of twinning and spinning; their unquiet surface conditions, the prevalence of spilling and spurting into space.

Second in importance is the recognition of the family relationships of stars — the tendency of a prevalent pattern to dominate a stellar group. A galactic cluster has a distinctive family picture; a globular cluster has an equally definite but quite different one. These family pictures attain an even broader significance when we see in them the mirrors of Populations I and II, which inhabit, respectively, the flattened arms and the spheroidal substratum of our galaxy, and of many other galaxies. A few galaxies seem to contain only Population I; probably the great majority are confined to Population II; and in the spirals we witness both populations in company. In the last chapter I suggested that this relation is only temporary, that the stars of Population I are bound up with the interstellar material of a more or less thin central layer in a spiral, and that they, and the spiral arms they populate, are evanescent features, fated to fade away and leave a more or less flattened, structureless system — an elliptical galaxy.

The third cardinal fact in speculating on stellar development is distance to the time horizon — an interval of something less than 10,000 million years, within which we may suppose that the character building of stars has been in progress.

Of these tangled threads it is our problem to weave a coherent web; and I must be frank — the web is full of holes at present, and if I were to attempt to foist it off as a well-woven fabric I should do it at the price not only of compromising with my own conscience, but also of incurring the derision of my astronomical colleagues. What I shall say about the development of stars is the result of my own gropings in the darkness of the subject. The gloom is fitfully illuminated by the light of many of the best minds in astronomy. The pioneers were Eddington, Jeans, and Russell. Among the torchbearers of today are Struve and von Weiszäcker, Ambartsumian and Krat, Hoyle and Lyttleton, Spitzer, Whipple, Schwarzschild, and Chandrasekhar. But their lights seem to lead in many directions, and some at any rate must be will-o'-the-wisps. I fear that I am not the least likely to be carrying an *ignis fatuus*.

From Population I to Population II. — In the last chapter I gave some of the reasons why I believe that Population I represents young stars — younger, at any rate, than Population II. I shall start from the premise that a rich galactic cluster, such as the great group

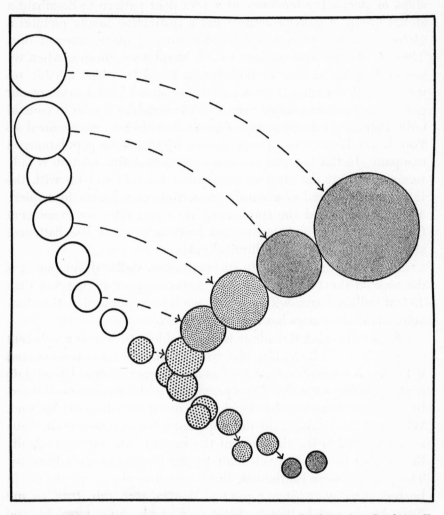

FIG. 11. *Speculative sketch of the course of development from Population I to Population II. These are only bare outlines for single stars; a star that divides may distribute itself along the main sequence. The downward curvature of the arrows denotes the onset of underluminosity. Sizes are on a conventional scale.*

in Perseus, represents a young family of stars of the same age, similar in birth and history. I suggest that in time — a very long time — this group will have developed the family traits characteristic of a globular cluster. I leave aside for the moment the enormous differences in size and population between the galactic and the globular clusters in our own system, only recalling that the Large Magellanic Cloud does seem to contain clusters that are "globular" in form but "galactic" in population. How are we to suppose the stellar characters to develop so that the first family portrait will transform into the second? We have here a problem like the child's word game that requires us to change "swan" into "bear" by a series of transformations that involve known words, such as swan-swat-seat-sear-bear. Can we visualize a series of steps by which one group portrait can pass, *through a series of known types of stars*, into another? If so, do they fit within the time framework that we have set up?

Let us take a close look at the population from which we propose to start. The most important fact about it is, I think, that the great majority of its members are small, faint, and of low mass. The great blue supergiants, even the stars like Sirius, are rare. At least down to stars a tenth of the brightness of the sun, we must imagine that the numbers continue to increase. If we compare the picture with that of the stars in the population with which we wish to finish, we notice *that the two diagrams seem to coalesce* for the faint stars, which are the preponderant members of the first and very likely of the second. This is not to say that there are no differences: Population II (if we are to judge from the high-velocity stars of our own neighborhood) includes large numbers of faint subdwarfs. But the two pictures differ much less for their fainter stars than for the stars higher up. And it is just these fainter stars that we have seen, when we considered the ages of things, to have very long life expectancies, longer than the interval since the time horizon; therefore they can be expected to have aged very slowly.

But when we turn to the rare, brilliant stars we find that the two diagrams have fanned apart. The brightest stars in galactic clusters, with almost a million times the luminosity of the sun, have no counterpart in Population II, where the best a star can achieve is a thousand times the sun's brightness. But, as we have seen, a star a million times as bright as the sun (if it fits the "mass-luminosity curve") has a very small life expectancy: ten million years would have bankrupted it. Two hundred million years would bankrupt the brightest of the Pleaides; the brightest of the Hyades have about 2000 million years to go. *The place where the diagrams for the two populations begin to fan apart is suspiciously near to the brightness of stars that would be bankrupted in an interval comparable to the distance from the time horizon.*

The factual basis for this attractive idea is very slender. Only two globular clusters have at present been surveyed down to the junction with the main sequence. And it is precisely when the data are meager that oversimplification is most tempting — and most treacherous. But, few as they are, these measures, by Baum, Arp, and Sandage, give a hint of a slight difference between the points of junction with the main sequence for the two clusters. The two may actually differ somewhat in age or history, for the pictures outlined by their variable stars differ too, as we shall see.

We can discern suggestive differences, not only between the main backbones of globular and galactic clusters, but also between those of individual galactic clusters. In some, the main sequence of stars runs up to tremendous luminosities, as in the twin Perseus clusters. In others, it seems to be shorn off — at high luminosities in the Pleaides, at lower brightness in the Hyades. Perhaps the highest point in a given cluster marks the stars that have exhausted their supplies. This idea, as will readily be seen, suggests that the great Perseus clusters are very young, the Pleaides not much older, and the Hyades-like clusters the oldest of the three. Perhaps it is no coincidence that the Hyades are the least compact and the least populous, the Perseus clusters the most concentrated and the richest, in the series.

Globular clusters, it will be remembered, are often rich in the rapidly vibrating RR Lyrae stars that are so characteristic of Population II, and seem to be strictly confined to that population. They contain also, in smaller numbers, the equally characteristic Population II variables of the so-called W Virginis and RV Tauri types, and a few — a very few — long-period variables. These pulsing stars in globular clusters have a family pattern all their own. They do not conform to the main backbone of the Population II family, which runs from cool, moderately bright stars toward fainter ones of higher temperature, and meets the main sequence near to the luminosity and color of the sun. They lie on, or above, a less conspicuous branch of the family, which runs almost horizontally across the family portrait at a level that corresponds to about a hundred times the sun's brightness. This branch contains some stars of high temperatures; a few, in fact, are actually hotter than main-sequence stars of similar brightness.

The RR Lyrae stars are confined to a limited domain of this horizontal branch; they are all very nearly of the same color and the same brightness. Therefore they must all be very nearly of the same size, though their periods of vibration range from about an hour and a half to almost a day. We may note in passing that this is a most remarkable fact. If the conventional rule, that the square of the period is inversely proportional to the mean density of a pulsating star, is valid for these RR Lyrae stars, the factor of 16 in the periods implies a factor of over 150 in mean density. We are fairly sure that these stars are all of about the same size, and (unless our simple period-density rule is at fault, which may quite possibly be the case) we can only attribute the large range in mean densities to an equally large variety among their masses. We do not know the mass of even one of the RR Lyrae stars; but as they are all of similar luminosity we can safely say, without knowing their actual masses, that some of them, at least, deviate from the mass-luminosity law. This, however, is a digression, to which we shall advert a little later, for other stars of Population II seem to depart from the usual relation between luminosity and mass.

The family pattern of the variable stars in globular clusters is our present concern. It was Martin Schwarzschild who made the important observation that RR Lyrae stars are found only within narrow limits of color and brightness, and this fact explains their total absence from some globular clusters, their presence by the hundred in others. For the horizontal branch of the family portrait may not run across at quite the same luminosity in all globular clusters. If it is present in a cluster, but does not cover the RR Lyrae domain, these stars will not appear in that particular cluster.

The luminosity of the horizontal branch of the globular-cluster family portrait does differ slightly from one cluster to another, and so does its richness in stars other than the pulsating variables. In fact, the two globular clusters that have been surveyed down to the main sequence differ not only in the point of junction, but also in variable-star population and in the level of the horizontal branch. Here is a possible index of the age and history of a globular cluster that is rich in possibilities, but it would be premature to expatiate on them. One can always put a straight line through two points; more data are needed before we can indulge ourselves in the luxuries of speculation.

The RR Lyrae stars are by far the commonest variables in globular clusters; the few W Virginis and RV Tauri stars are known, largely through the work of A. H. Joy, to be luminous yellow stars. They show relations between behavior, color, luminosity, and period that are far more complicated than the familiar period-luminosity curve of the Cepheids. These variables in clusters are pulsating too, but their behavior is distinctively different from that of the Cepheids.

Variable stars in globular clusters have their well-known counterparts in Population II of the substratum of our galaxy. These luminous yellow variables "pulsate" in waves that pass off successively from the stellar surface; for a short time both waves can be seen at once, one *through* the other, as was discovered by R. F. Sanford at Mount Wilson. No Cepheid variable behaves in this manner; but the RR Lyrae stars (also of Population II) do the same thing, as Sanford and Struve have both shown; in these stars the two rising waves coexist for a mere twenty minutes, and their detection was a great feat of observation.

The Cepheids, characteristic variable stars of Population I, have a simpler family pattern which is defined by the period-luminosity law. The most rapidly vibrating Cepheids rarely have periods of less than two days, in strong contrast to the 90-minute RR Lyrae stars. The ascending pattern of luminosity with period rises to its greatest height for periods longer than those found for most Population II variables of comparable brightness.

I have placed the Cepheid variables in Population I: they share the rotary motion within the galaxy, and cling to the galactic plane.

But *not one Cepheid has been found in a galactic cluster*. It is quite true that Cepheids are rare in our system of stars, but they are among the most luminous of stars, and a good portion of luminous stars are members of galactic clusters. Ambartsumian considers that the high proportion of 90 percent of all very luminous hot stars are members of what he calls *associations*, but he notes that Cepheids are absent from these groups. The same seems to be true even of the Magellanic Clouds, which are vastly richer than our own system in Cepheids: the Cepheid variables do not concentrate in the same districts as the dense knots of bright, hot stars and nebulosity.

If we hope to fit the Cepheid variables into the general pattern of Population I, we must conclude, I think, that they are somewhat older than the main-sequence stars of similar brightness in the galactic-cluster diagram that we took as the starting point for the family line-up of Population I. They are not associated with the very youngest groups.

Another observation goes to strengthen this view. The hot, bright stars outline the spiral arms of our galaxy, for they illuminate the bright nebulae by whose light Morgan has photographed the arms. But the Cepheids are not confined to narrow arms. Their distribution appears to follow the curve of the arm, but instead of falling along a narrow line, they are spread into a wide band. The same impression is given by the bright Cepheids that were discovered by Hubble in the outer parts of the galaxy in Andromeda, which is in many ways so like our own. The Cepheids do not fall into narrow lines, as do the bright nebulae photographed by Baade, which look almost like beads on a string. The Cepheids may have been born in the narrow lanes, but they have lived long enough to move a small distance from them — not far enough to form a very thick layer in the central plane, but far enough to blur the sharp outline of the arm.

If the Cepheids of Population I transform gradually into the yellow variables of Population II, the route by which they travel eludes us. The only clue that we have is that (if they maintain similar luminosity during the transformation) they grow somewhat smaller with age. Perhaps in their final stages they derive some of their light from contraction, a suggestion that we shall meet for other stars later in the chapter.

Between the Two Populations. — Another group of variable stars presents us with an unsolved mystery. These are the long-period variables, diffuse and large, of low density and low temperature, fainter than the brightest Cepheids or RV Tauri stars. They are not found in galactic clusters, and rarely (if ever) in globular clusters, so we must base our conclusions on their behavior within the galaxy. In motion and in distribution they fall between the two populations; in fact, they fill the whole gap between them.

Here we clearly have stars in various stages of transition. They are the most interesting and the most puzzling group of all. One thing, however, they do bring home to us. The two populations are not sharply divided at all levels. We have seen that there is little division for the numerous, very faint stars; it is interesting that some of the least luminous variable stars show a blurring of the outlines too. But we must not forget that the RR Lyrae stars, which are no brighter than the long-period variables, are quite clearly confined to Population II.

Observed Changes of Stars. — So far we have merely taken two extreme types of stellar group portrait, and attempted to stretch the one to the shape of the other. Incidentally it will be noted that we have tacitly rubbed out the brightest stars of the first population, and left nothing but stars up to two thousand times as bright as the sun. We are not justified in distorting the facts, so to speak, in this way, or in throwing some out altogether, unless we can show that the nature of the stars themselves makes them capable of the corresponding changes.

Let us summarize the changes that we either observe stars to undergo, or suppose them to undergo.

If stars do indeed subsist on their own internal hydrogen, *they must maintain their masses almost unaltered.* For the whole of the hydrogen is not destroyed: it is frozen (if I may so speak of a process that takes place at 20 million degrees) into helium, and the total loss of mass is about 0.7 percent. Even if a star were all hydrogen, it would lose only this fraction by converting all its mass into helium. It follows that a star will always have essentially the same mass (so far as its nuclear consumption of hydrogen is concerned), and if it conforms to the mass-luminosity law throughout its life, it will not only keep up its brightness, but will actually grow a little brighter with increasing mean molecular weight, as described in the first chapter. Therefore, so long as it is sustained by the carbon cycle or some similar hydrogen diet, and follows the mass-luminosity rule, it will keep on the same horizontal line in the conventional picture (Fig. 10) that shows brightness plotted against temperature or size, or will even rise a little above it.

If a star always keeps almost the same mass, and follows the mass-luminosity law, *it will always, therefore, be of about the same brightness.* On this assumption, once a bright star, always a bright star (until bankruptcy supervenes), and any permissible stretching or distortion of the family portrait will be *horizontal or upward.*

This statement presumes that the star is kept well stirred, so that new hydrogen atoms keep moving in to replace those that have been used up. A star that is not well stirred (and rotation very likely promotes stirring) may grow rather fainter and possibly cooler at the surface as time goes on — perhaps, in the end, much fainter.

So much for what we think a star *can* do. What are stars actually observed to be doing? Most spectacular, perhaps, is the throwing off of material. Rapidly spinning stars whirl off atoms from their surfaces, and the zones of glowing atoms can be seen around some eclipsing stars such as RW Tauri. For other stars, a growing number in fact, the spectroscope gives evidence of the ejection of atoms, sometimes in a steady shower, sometimes in spurts. These observations should give us no surprise when we remember the sun with its never-ending play of prominences, surges, spicules, and the like. And we should not forget the more spectacular ejections, the cataclysms that tear off the whole surfaces of novae, following some explosive burst below the surface. The brilliant novae undergo these cataclysms perhaps once in a million years; but milder novae do so every decade or so, and the so-called dwarf novae repeat the process on a smaller scale every few weeks.

Have we here an example of rapid loss of mass that could displace the stars vertically on the diagram as well as horizontally? That matter is lost is a certainty; but when we measure it we find that the cataclysm falls very short of a catastrophe; at each burst the star loses perhaps one thousandth of its material. At the rate of one outburst in a million years, we can see that a serious reduction in weight would need an interval not very different from the interval since the time horizon. The novae, besides, are rather exceptional stars, at least from our insular standpoint as members of Population I. Their distribution, and perhaps their motions, place them in Population II, and between outbursts they have much in common with the subdwarfs. I suspect that they have taken a long time to get to their present stage.

We have learned to think that Population II is old, and perhaps the novae represent the final struggles of stars that are well on their way to bankruptcy. They still possess a certain amount of hydrogen, at least on their surfaces, so they are not completely down and out, though they may have less within. But perhaps each outburst marks a step on the downward path; they may suffer explosions of smaller and smaller intensity, and at progressively shorter intervals, and move in the process from normal novae to recurrent nova, finally to end as dwarf novae with a mild outburst every few weeks. As to what happens after that I should not hazard a guess.

There are, however, explosions of quite another order, that seem to be real stellar catastrophes — the supernovae, which literally commit suicide, and blow most of their substance violently into space. The remains of one such stellar catastrophe are to be seen today, still scattering into space. The remains of the star are still there, apparently a white dwarf — the Crab Nebula (Plate 27), debris of the supernova explosion observed in A.D. 1054. Supernovae must fit into the pattern in quite a different place from ordinary novae. They are rare — perhaps one in a galaxy in several centuries; only one star in ten thousand in our own system would (on this basis) have been a supernova since the time horizon. Supernovae, then, cannot be our only source of white dwarfs, for probably there are well over a hundred times as many white dwarfs as this in our stellar system.

It is certain that many stars, from novae down, are steadily or spasmodically throwing off material into space. But it hardly looks as if they are throwing it off in quantities great enough to displace them very much in the group picture. They move downward a little as they spill and splutter; but they can hardly move far.

How about the opposite possibility, that stars are picking up material as they move through space, feeding on the interstellar dust and gas? It is possible for a star to do exactly this, but the conditions have to be just right. If a star is too hot it will blow the potential food away; if it is moving too fast it will miss the feast. A fair estimate is that a star must be more massive than the sun, not too hot, and stay within a dense cloud for at least ten million years, if it is to pick up an appreciable amount of interstellar food. Probably not many stars fulfill these conditions, and I doubt whether the consumption of dust and smoke is an important factor in increasing the masses of stars, and therefore causing them to move upward in the diagram.

Nutrition of Red Giants. — Are there any unknown nuclear processes that might sustain the stars, in addition to the consumption of hydrogen? There are several possible ones, such as subsistence on lithium, beryllium, and boron, and these would go forward at low temperatures, which, as we shall see, would make things easier for the giants (or at least for astronomers trying to understand the giants!). But the trouble with these processes is a scarcity of materials. They could not possibly sustain the stars for very long. Stellar infants probably feed on them for a time. But for a steady stellar diet, hydrogen is the only one among the atoms that fills the bill, for the simple reason that almost all the universe is made of hydrogen.

The problem of nutrition of the red-giant stars is particularly acute. It hinges on the rather technical question of the stars' internal structure. If the red giants are built like the stars of the main sequence, their internal temperatures (which depend on the ratio of mass to radius) must be fairly low, too low to actuate the carbon cycle that consumes hydrogen. The proton-proton reaction might serve, but it has other problems, and the question is still *sub judice.* Is there any way of releasing energy within red giants?

There are two schools of thought (and each has its own ramifications) on this knotty question. The supporters of one seek to "fix up" the centers of the giant stars in various ways so that they will have the necessary high temperatures; and to some extent the trick can be done, though no one has yet succeeded in imagining a model that will keep the *extreme* red supergiants going. Another school is beginning to turn back to the contraction hypothesis that was devised over fifty years ago to account for the sun's continued vigor. The sun is a star of low mass; perhaps a more massive star, which has therefore more available gravitational energy, might be able to sustain itself on contraction for longer periods. The variable stars, for example, may perhaps be contracting. Of the two sequences of variable stars, characteristic of Populations I and II, the members of the second sequence, at the same luminosity, are about one fourth the size of those of the first. We do not know how a star that was subsisting partly on contraction would feel about the mass-luminosity law, and quite possibly the variable stars do not conform to it. We have no measure of the mass of a periodic variable star, and their unique behavior suggests that they differ in some definite way from other stars of similar brightness. Contraction might conceivably be associated with pulsation. But one thing is sure: if these stars are contracting, they are doing so very slowly, or their periods would be changing noticeably. Certainly the RR Lyrae stars are undergoing some interesting internal adjustments, for they are all of the same brightness and the same size, though their densities (if we are to trust the well-known relation of period to density) must differ by a large factor, as we saw earlier.

If contraction is to supply a star with energy for an appreciable time, it must reduce the interior to the condition of a white dwarf. Thus a developing giant may finally reach the supernova stage, and a final explosion lay bare the degenerate core.

The problem of red-giant stars is somewhat clarified when we realize that there are giants and giants. The aura of high-luminosity red supergiants about the twin Perseus clusters must be a group of extremely youthful stars. We have seen reason to think these clusters very young, and their huge red members may be true spendthrifts of small life expectancy.

The large, diffuse Population I stars, such as Aldebaran and Capella, have longer life expectancies, but still not very long. Capella "conforms" to the mass-luminosity relation, and its life expectancy, *at the present rate of expenditure*, is seen from Table 1 to be 20 million years.

But the large red stars that head the backbone of the family portrait of a globular cluster are a very different problem. If we are right in supposing that such a family group is very old, how have these red stars survived, and what has kept them going? Even if their structure can be adjusted to meet the requirements of the carbon cycle, their life expectancies are only of the same order as that of Capella, if their masses dictate their luminosities in the usual manner. And this interval is shorter than the supposed age of a globular cluster by a factor of ten at least.

Let it be admitted at once that the spectra of the bright, cool stars in globular clusters (so far as the very difficult problem of recording them has been resolved) are definitely not similar to those of Population I stars of similar color and brightness. The chemical composition of the Population II stars seems to differ significantly, and perhaps they actually do contain less hydrogen, a sign of partial exhaustion of food supply.

Even more important information is given by the few high-velocity stars (which are therefore members of Population II) that are red giants, and are probably comparable to the red giants of globular clusters. We saw in Chapter 6 that Arcturus, best-known of these stars, is *underluminous*. It does not conform to the mass-luminosity law, and its life expectancy is correspondingly increased. The figure given in Table 1 for Arcturus, 50 million years, is not large enough to stretch to the time horizon, but it is a move in that direction. Other high-velocity red giants seem to be underluminous also, as was discovered by Keenan. Perhaps the bright red stars in globular clusters are all more massive than their luminosities, and the mass-luminosity law, would lead us to expect.

If the bright stars in globular clusters are underluminous, they not only receive an increased lease of life, but they suggest a possible answer to the question what becomes of the bright supergiants of Population I? Galactic clusters, as we have seen, do not contain only main-sequence stars. Many contain red giants, and in each cluster the red giants seem to lie at about the level in the family portrait at which the main sequence comes to an end in the upward direction. Are we witnessing the beginning of progress toward a population of red-giant stars? Possibly the red giants in the Hyades have larger masses than their brightness indicates. Perhaps they represent steps taken by stars such as Rigel or the bright members of the Pleiades as bankruptcy approaches — first steps that will ultimately carry them to the head of a family of Population II. They may be sustained by a combination of declining nuclear processes and contraction, with contraction finally assuming the major role.

After this brief survey of the possible processes that can change stars, let me summarize my own opinion by saying that loss of mass by ejection, or gain of mass by feeding on interstellar matter, can be important only for very few stars, and are not a major factor in general stellar development. The consumption of hydrogen, and the ultimate exhaustion of the supply, are the main causes of stellar change; for the red giants neither the study of special models nor that of the possibilities of contraction have gone far enough to lead to a definite conclusion, but some red giants may exist for cosmically long intervals if they become underluminous and draw energy from contraction. From this point of view, the course of stellar development is determined at the very outset; the stars start out with essentially the masses that they are to have through life, and more small stars are born than large ones.

The Birth of a Star. — So we come back to the problem of the birth of stars. The ideas of stellar origins are converging in the same way as the ideas of the origin of the solar system. Gone is the picture of fifty years ago, when we thought of the earth as the child of the sun; now we see her as the sun's small sister. We took the development of galaxies back to the primeval eddies of gas, and I think that the stars must have formed as part of the same process from dust and grains within the gas. This, I imagine, is why the oldest members of the stellar system (as I suppose the globular clusters to be) are so large and populous, for the available material was richer then. As the layer of dust and gas sank toward the galactic plane, stars continued to form. Dust and gas still lie dense in a thin layer, and stars are still being formed there. The motions of the dust, its density, and the light of the stars nearby, all determine whether a star will form. Probably the birth of a star, from dust to luminescence, takes about a million years.

What are these primitive stars like? They must contract into globes, slowly at first, but with increasing speed, until at last they heat up rapidly, the temperature within rises to the level of nuclear cookery, and the star becomes a star. If we are to look for such stars, we must search the thin layer in the galactic plane for stars that are hot, with envelopes in violent motion. Are the Wolf-Rayet stars the newborn? They cling to the galactic plane; they people the spiral arms. They are particularly common in the younger Magellanic Cloud, the Large one; they fit the other conditions.

But there is another place where we see stars that may well be in the birth process. Within some of the large, dark nebulae, such as those in Taurus and Orion, we see peculiar stars, surrounded by streaks of luminous gas, that may be stars in process of formation. There seem too many of them to be chance travelers passing through the cloud and picking up matter as they go, though some astronomers prefer that explanation. In any case, when we look at the established stellar population, we cannot deny that small, faint stars must have been formed in the greatest numbers.

What will be the adventures of the newborn star? The chances are that it will be rotating, because eddies must have assisted at its birth. Some theories of stellar development hinge on this rotation, which they see as leading ultimately to the stars' splitting in two — perhaps in several steps that lead to a multiple system such as that of Castor. Because the enormous majority of stars are double, no picture of evolution is satisfactory unless it accounts for the stellar preference for company. If most stars were formed by the splitting of rapidly spinning primitive stars, this condition would be met; and it is very significant that the bright, hot stars are spinning the fastest (and spinning almost without exception), whereas stars like the sun, and fainter, have very little rotation, unless they are members of close pairs.

Another advantage of the idea that newly formed stars spin rapidly, and divide, is that it provides a way of moving them down the main sequence. The mass-luminosity law states that the luminosity is proportional to a little over the cube of the mass. So if a star splits into two equal halves, and both continue to conform to the law, each will have only one eighth of the brightness of the

147

original star. If the process were repeated several times the resulting stars might be distributed in widely different parts of the main sequence, like the components of Castor.

Strange Bedfellows among the Stars. — But the matter is not quite so simple. This explanation will not account for Sirius. The companion weighs less than Sirius, and if (as seems likely) it has always weighed less, it should be less far along the road to bankruptcy, instead of having arrived there. One may speculate that it was originally formed from matter that was very low in hydrogen.

This picture of the formation of the Sirius system suggests that Sirius and its companion were never one; they were formed together out of material of nonuniform composition. Another school of thought than the one that derives binary stars from splitting supposes that double stars were not formed from the division of a single one, but were born together at the same time from the interstellar dust. This view has something to commend it; nobody can suppose, for instance, that a star cluster was formed from the fission of a rotating star; and some systems like that of Sirius almost seem to require individual origins. But I do not think that the evidence on the prevalent rotation of the bright, hot stars, and the virtual disappearance of rotation for stars a little fainter than Sirius, coupled with the large numbers of binary stars that are almost in contact, can be explained except by splitting.

There is another possible route by which Sirius and its companion may have reached their present stages. If the Sirius system was once a pair like Algol, or even like Zeta Aurigae (Fig. 7), it consisted of a main-sequence star and a star of smaller life expectancy. The red component of Algol, if it resembles those of similar unlike stellar twins, is probably *overluminous*. Many Algol-like pairs certainly have this peculiarity, as Struve has emphasized. Perhaps Sirius B has reached white-dwarfdom because it was a spendthrift: its luminosity was out of proportion to its mass (as anticipated from the mass-luminosity "law"), and it exhausted its supply before its main-sequence companion. This suggestion is not an explanation, for it leaves us with another problem: what is the history of a system that contains one normal and one overluminous star? Struve has made the suggestion that such pairs are newly formed and have not had the time to "settle down." But though our idea does not provide a fundamental explanation, it suggests how we can derive one type of system from another known type of system, so that two problems are potentially reduced to one.

Perhaps we are coming to the belief that the mass-luminosity relation is primarily a characteristic of main-sequence stars. Most double stars, whose masses can be measured, are members of this sequence. Some, at least, of the subgiants, as well as some supergiants, are overluminous; some Population II stars are underluminous. It is only too likely that in our quest for regularity we have oversimplified the relation between luminosity and mass, and have thus overlooked some of the deviations that hold the key to our problem. Most of the stars that we know to be overluminous — diffuse components of Algol stars, and components of W Ursae Majoris systems (dwarf twins) — are members of close pairs, which is a mark of relative youth. The W Ursae Majoris stars are also spinning very rapidly, another character that we are beginning to associate with recent origin. And the suspicion is arising (though on more slender evidence, for we have no direct knowledge of their masses) that bright Population II stars tend to be underluminous. Possibly overluminosity is a characteristic of very young stars, and underluminosity of very old ones. But other factors, as yet incompletely understood, must modify such a tendency. Mass, rotation, internal structure, and original composition must be involved, and they are probably interconnected also.

A Possible Course for Stellar Development. — Let me end by sketching the development of stars, a highly personal view. They are formed from the interstellar dust, the majority small at birth, a few large, a very few enormous. The protostars contract rapidly, heat up, and begin to shine, most of them as main-sequence stars. The youthful stars, born of dust within the eddying gas, and played upon by localized radiations of other stars, come into being with a tendency to rotation. Those that rotate rapidly undergo division (perhaps in the prestellar stage, perhaps after they have already begun to shine), and distribute themselves along the main sequence. All these stars are of the same structure, but the heavier ones are rather hotter at the center. They proceed to consume their hydrogen,

149

each at the rate prescribed by its mass. The population resembles that of a galactic cluster.

As the brighter stars use up their hydrogen and go toward exhaustion, they move off the main sequence toward the right if they are not rotating, and are therefore poorly mixed. At the same time they begin to build up large envelopes, and become giant stars, which may gradually decline in luminosity, and ultimately line up as the giant sequence of the globular-cluster population (Population II). The variable stars are somehow involved in this transition, but I confess I do not know what distinguishes them from the non-variable red giants. They seem to be uniformly brighter, color for color, and this must reflect some difference, but whether of structure or composition I should not like to guess. I suspect that the variable stars of Population I are the ancestors of those of Population II, but the huge number of RR Lyrae stars in the latter needs explaining, and I am not sure that the observed number of Cepheids is in harmony with the idea. However, it is very interesting to notice that the Small Magellanic Cloud (which, as we have seen, seems older than the Large) contains great numbers of Cepheids of very short period, perhaps on their way to becoming RR Lyrae stars.

For every few stars that move to the right and become giants, probably some move slightly to the left, and in time become subdwarfs, poorer in hydrogen than the main sequence, and typical of Population II. These stars, at least some of them, are probably the stars that finally become novae, and propel themselves down the subdwarf sequence with diminishing outbursts at shortening intervals. The final end of these stars should be the white-dwarf stage. It is interesting that most of the white dwarfs that are members of binaries have faint red stars as companions. A few known white dwarfs that are coupled with brighter main-sequence stars such as Sirius and Procyon, or even with red-giant variables such as Mira Ceti, represent a different problem.

The theoretical astronomers have shown convincingly that only stars less massive than about one-and-a-half times the sun are able to reach the white-dwarf stage. A heavier star that exhausts its supply of hydrogen must presumably find another way out. Possibly the outburst of a supernova represents the liquidation of such a star.

Such is the highly personalized picture. I am only too conscious that it is out of drawing, that the chiaroscuro is improperly treated, and that I have laid the color on too thickly in some places and neglected others. I have at least made a crude attempt at naturalism, and have striven to avoid the influence of the nonobjective school that relies on theories of what *ought to be*, rather than on the observation of what *is*.

A final question: where is it all headed? What will be the ultimate fate of the stellar universe? I can look forward with some pleasure to a world of symmetrical, structureless, elliptical galaxies, pure Population II. Long after that, perhaps, will come pure white-dwarf population for the less massive stars, enlivened by sporadic supernovae as the more massive stars pass to their rest. One thing seems clear. Such a universe cannot be rejuvenated. The white dwarfs are in a blind alley; their material is truly degenerate; they cannot even solidify. If the imagined conditions at the beginning are beyond conception, so are those at the end — but in a different way. Fortunately it is far in the future, further than the time horizon of the past. Perhaps we are wrong in thinking that it can happen at all. Science has a long way to go yet.

> *Awake, awake! The world is young*
> *For all its weary years of thought.*
> *The starkest fights must still be fought,*
> *The most surprising songs be sung.*

Suggestions for Further Reading

Bart J. Bok and Priscilla F. Bok, *The Milky Way* (Harvard Books on Astronomy, Harvard University Press). A popular but authoritative account of methods and results in the study of our own galaxy.

Harlow Shapley, *Galaxies* (Harvard Books on Astronomy, Harvard University Press). An account of the study of galaxies by a leading authority.

Leo Goldberg and Lawrence Aller, *Atoms, Stars, and Nebulae* (Harvard Books on Astronomy, Harvard University Press). A simply written account of the physical nature of cosmic bodies.

Donald H. Menzel, *Our Sun* (Harvard Books on Astronomy, Harvard University Press). A detailed popular account of the sun and solar phenomena.

Leon Campbell and Luigi Jacchia, *The Story of Variable Stars* (Harvard Books on Astronomy, Harvard University Press). A general account of the nature and behavior of variable stars.

William Marshall Smart, *Some Famous Stars* (New York: Longmans, Green, 1951). Detailed accounts of several crucial stars and their relationships.

Fred Hoyle, *The Nature of the Universe* (New York: Harper and Brothers, 1951). A popular discussion by a theoretical astronomer, whose views differ in many ways from those expressed in the present book.

C. F. von Weizsäcker, *The History of Nature* (Chicago: University of Chicago Press, 1949). A popular book of much wider scope than the present; it treats of the relation of man to the universe in all its aspects.

Otto Struve, *Stellar Evolution* (Princeton: Princeton University Press, 1950). A more technical book than any of the preceding, by a leading astronomer. It contains much of the basic material that bears on stellar evolution, and arrives at several theories as to its course.

Suggestions for Further Reading

Index

Numbers in italics refer to plates.

Plates

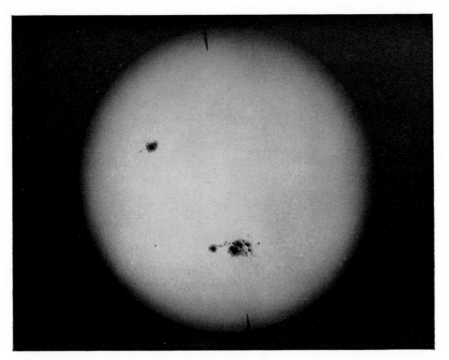

PLATE 1. *The sun, with several sunspots, the largest group ever recorded (January 24, 1926).* (*Mount Wilson Observatory.*)

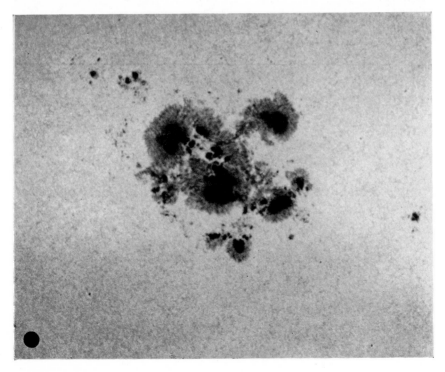

PLATE 2. *A group of sunspots. The centers look dark only by contrast. They are a little cooler than surrounding regions, but still intensely bright. Note the fine granulation all over the sun's surface. The black disk represents the size of the earth.* (*Mount Wilson Observatory.*)

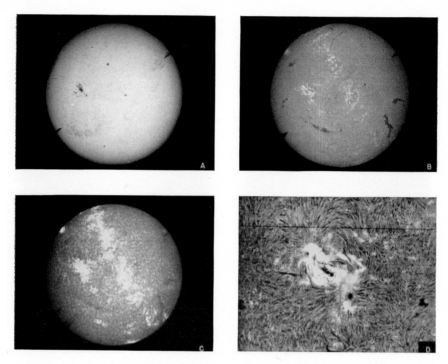

PLATE 3. *Three photographs of the sun, made almost simultaneously in light of different colors: (a) taken in light of all colors from green to violet; (b) in the red light of hydrogen; (c) in the violet light of calcium. In the lower right (d) is an enlarged hydrogen picture that shows unusually fine detail. (Mount Wilson Observatory.)*

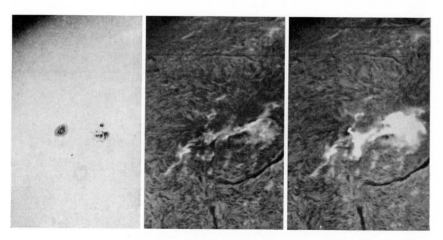

PLATE 4. *The solar flare of August 8, 1937. The first picture is an ordinary photograph of the sunspot group; the second shows the region in red hydrogen light; the third, taken 11 minutes later, shows the flare at maximum intensity. (Mount Wilson Observatory.)*

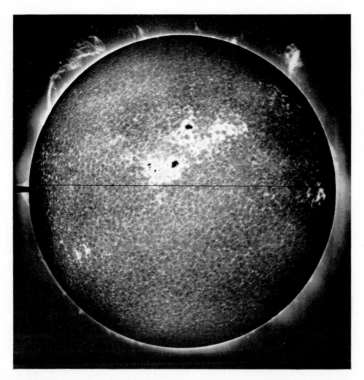

PLATE 5. *Disk of the sun, photographed in violet calcium light. The picture shows sunspots, the surrounding disturbed regions, and prominences around the sun's rim. (Mount Wilson Observatory.)*

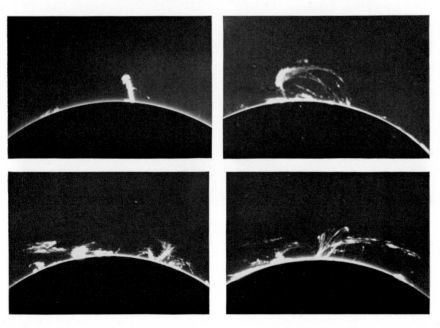

PLATE 6. *Four types of solar prominences. Top left: a pillar; lower left: treelike formations; top right: funnel type near an active sunspot; lower right: loops in the neighborhood of sunspots. The material seen in all these pictures is being sucked in toward the sun. (High Altitude Observatory, Harvard University and University of Colorado.)*

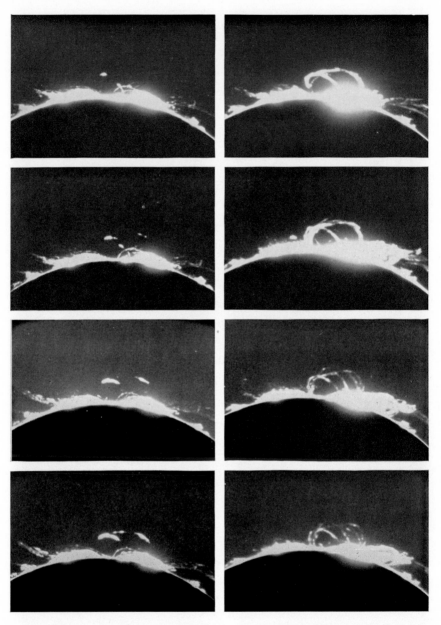

PLATE 7. *Development of a loop prominence; the two successive columns read downward. The whole series of events took place in about two hours. The fourth picture of Plate 6 shows the same region two days later. (High Altitude Observatory, Harvard University and University of Colorado.)*

PLATE 8. *The sun's corona, photographed at the total eclipse of May 28, 1900.*

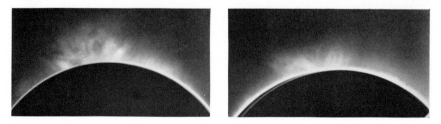

PLATE 9. *Photograph of the sun's corona in the light of iron atoms that have lost thirteen electrons (left) and nine electrons (right). Note the difference in structure between the two pictures. (Lyot, Pic du Midi Observatory.)*

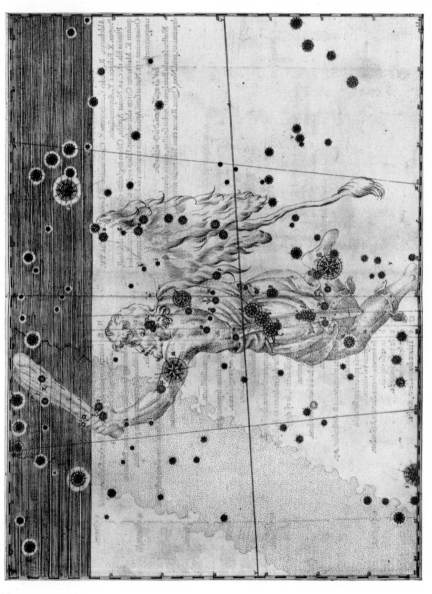

PLATE 10. The constellation of Orion, as portrayed in Bayer's Uranometria, 1603. Bayer was the first to assign Greek letters to the stars, and we still use his designations. Betelgeuse is labelled α, Rigel is β.

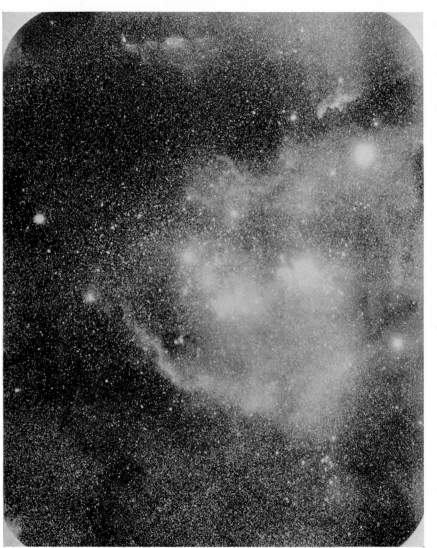

PLATE 11. *Photograph of the constellation Orion. The bright stars in Bayer's picture can be identified. Notice that Betelgeuse is faint on the photograph because of its redness, a sign of low temperature. The whole constellation is wreathed in bright nebulosity. (F. E. Ross, Yerkes Observatory.)*

PLATE 12. *View toward the center of our galactic system, in the constellations Scorpio and Ophiuchus. The figure of the Scorpion can be traced among the stars. Note the brilliant star clouds, overlaid by patches of dark material. Rings around the stars are spurious photographic effects. (Composite photograph, Boyden Station, Harvard Observatory.)*

PLATE 13. *Part of the southern Milky Way. The Southern Cross is left of the center; two of its stars are red, and therefore faint on the photograph; the eye sees all four stars of the Cross about equally bright. The Coal Sack is below the Cross to the left; just above it is the galactic cluster Kappa Crucis (Plate 33). At the right is the brilliant Eta Carinae nebulosity (Plate 16). At the extreme left is Beta Centauri; the bright diffuse object, upper left, is the globular cluster Omega Centauri (Plates 37 and 38). (Boyden Station, Harvard Observatory.)*

PLATE 14. *Enlarged view of part of Plate 12. At the upper right are the bright stars Alpha and Beta Centauri. The former (which is multiple) is the nearest star to the sun; the latter is very distant. Near the lower left is an elongated galactic cluster; its members are very brilliant, but appear faint because they are far away. (Boyden Station, Harvard Observatory.)*

PLATE 15. *Enlarged portion of the region shown in Plate 13. Two bright stars of the Southern Cross are seen at the top and at the right; near the top is Kappa Crucis. The Coal Sack is seen below; notice the definite bounds of the dark material. (Boyden Station, Harvard Observatory.)*

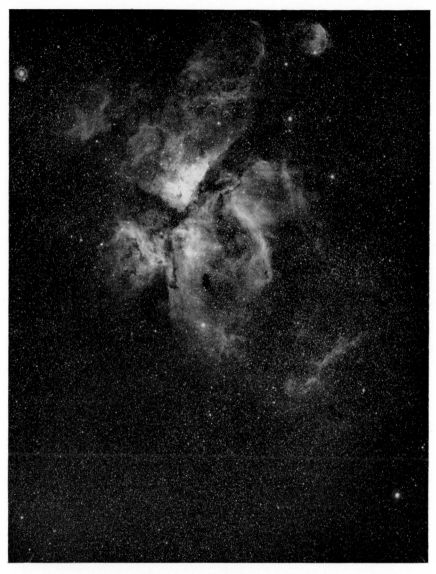

PLATE 16. *The Eta Carinae region of the southern Milky Way, photographed on a red-sensitive plate. Notice the intricate distribution of the bright and dark nebulosity. (Bester, Armagh-Dunsink-Harvard telescope, Boyden Station, Harvard Observatory.)*

PLATE 17. *Enlargement of a portion of Plate 16, to show the details of the nebulosity.*

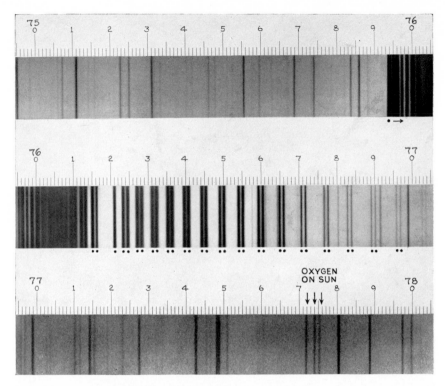

PLATE 18. *Part of the spectrum of the sun (infrared light), showing the regularly spaced pattern of colors that is cut from sunlight by the molecules of oxygen in our atmosphere; the principal features of this pattern are marked with dots. In the lowest strip, three lines that come from the oxygen atom in the sun's atmosphere are marked with arrows. The numbers refer to the wavelength of the light (in Angstrom units, 10^{-8} cm.). (Mount Wilson Observatory.)*

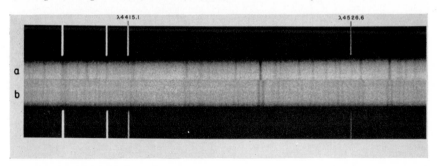

PLATE 19. *Spectrum of a spectroscopic binary star, Zeta Ursa Majoris (Mizar). Spectral type, A2; period, 20.5 days. (a) June 11, 1927; lines of the two components superimposed. (b) June 13, 1927; lines of the two components separated by a difference in orbital velocity of 140 km/sec. (Mount Wilson Observatory.)*

PLATE 20. *The "North America" nebula, which lies in the constellation Cygnus, the Swan, and is excited to luminescence by the bright star Deneb. (B. J. Bok, Jewett telescope, Harvard Observatory.)*

PLATE 21. *The Pleiades, a cluster of rather hot stars, surrounded by a cloud that reflects and scatters their light. Notice the fine shredding and streaking of the cloud. The rays from the stars are an instrumental effect. (Crossley reflector, Lick Observatory.)*

PLATE 22. *The "Horsehead" nebula in the constellation Orion. The brilliant interface between two dark clouds is probably caused to glow by the energy of collision of the clouds. (Mount Wilson Observatory.)*

PLATE 23. The "Great Nebula" of Orion, surrounding the middle star of Orion's sword (see Plates 10 and 11). It is caused to glow by a knot of very hot stars, the "Trapezium." (Mount Wilson Observatory).

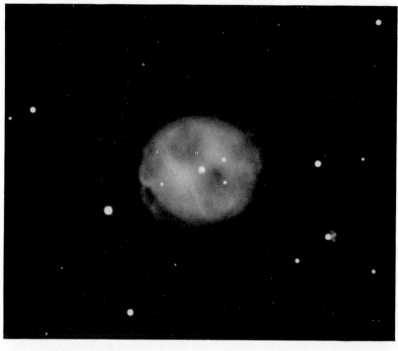

PLATE 25. The "Owl" nebula in Ursa Major, another example of a slowly expanding envelope around a very hot star. The structure is more complex than that of the "Ring" nebula in Lyra. (Mount Wilson Observatory.)

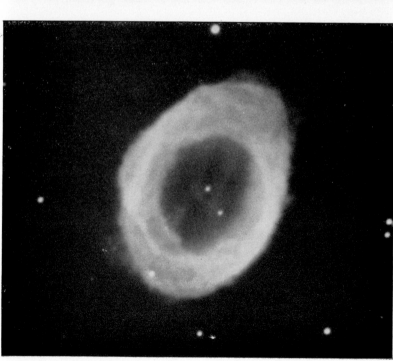

PLATE 24. The "Ring" nebula in Lyra, an enormous gaseous envelope around a star of very high temperature. (Mount Wilson Observatory.)

PLATE 26. *The nebulosity produced by the explosion of Nova Persei 1901, photographed about fifty years after the outburst was observed. The expanding gases are probably stimulated to shine by the energy of collision with thin interstellar gas clouds. (Palomar Observatory.)*

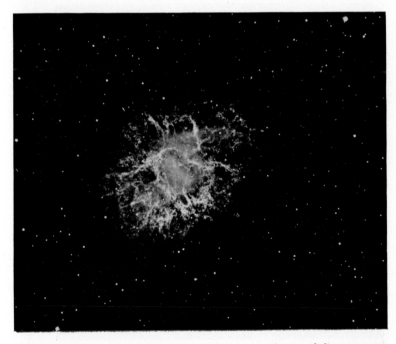

PLATE 27. *The "Crab" nebula in Taurus, the remains of an exploding supernova photographed about 900 years after the event. The speed of explosion is about 600 miles a second. Notice the wild turbulence of the ejected gases. (Palomar Observatory.)*

PLATE 28. *The constellation Cassiopeia, as portrayed by Bayer in 1603. The familiar bright "W" of stars in the constellation can be recognized, but the brightest star in the picture is the supernova that was seen in 1572, and has now completely disappeared.*

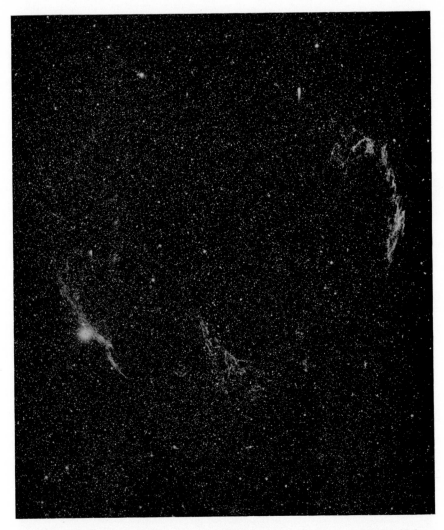

PLATE 29. *The "Network" nebula in the constellation Cygnus, the Swan. Finely shredded gas clouds pervade the whole picture. They show outward expansion, and are probably the remnants of a stellar explosion in the remote past.* (*J. G. Baker and Simone D. Gossner, Jewett telescope, Harvard Observatory.*)

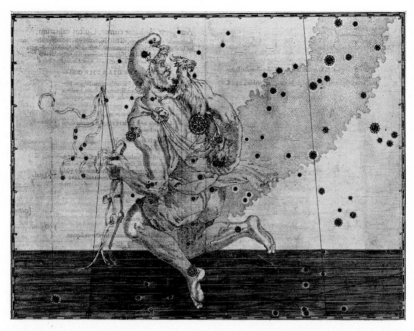

PLATE 30. *The constellation Auriga, the Charioteer, from Bayer's Uranometria. The brightest star, a, is Capella. The stars ε and ζ are two of the gigantic eclipsing systems shown in Fig. 7, p. 62.*

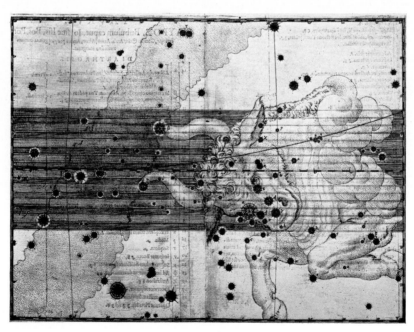

PLATE 31. *The constellation Taurus, the Bull, from Bayer's Uranometria. The Hyades form the nose of the Bull; the Pleiades can be seen higher up on his shoulder. The shaded strip marks the path of the sun among the stars; the stippled band marks the Milky Way.*

PLATE 32. *The great double cluster in Perseus. (Harvard Observatory.)*

PLATE 33. *The galactic cluster Kappa Crucis, the "Jewel Box."* (*Boyden Station, Harvard Observatory.*)

PLATE 34. *The star clouds in Sagittarius, toward the center of our galaxy. The "Trifid" nebula is to the left, Messier 8 to the right. (B. J. Bok, Armagh-Dunsink-Harvard telescope, Boyden Station, Harvard Observatory.)*

PLATE 35. *The great cluster of hot stars, surrounded by bright nebulosity flecked with dark globules, that is known as Messier 8. (Lick Observatory.)*

PLATE 36. *The "Tarantula" nebula, a cluster of brilliant stars, meshed in nebulosity, in the Large Magellanic Cloud (see Plates 46 and 48). It is comparable in size and brilliance to the whole constellation of Orion. (B. J. Bok, Armagh-Dunsink-Harvard telescope, Boyden Station, Harvard Observatory.)*

PLATE 37. *The globular cluster Omega Centauri; a short exposure with the 60-inch telescope. (Boyden Station, Harvard Observatory.)*

PLATE 38. *The globular cluster, Omega Centauri, photographed with a longer exposure on a red-sensitive plate. The scale is a little smaller than that of Plate 37. (W. D. Victor, Armagh-Dunsink-Harvard telescope, Boyden Station, Harvard Observatory.)*

PLATE 39. *The great spiral galaxy in Andromeda. The two elliptical companions may be seen, one below the spiral, one superimposed upon it. (Palomar Observatory.)*

PLATE 40. *The central regions of the Andromeda galaxy, showing the inner parts of the arms and the brilliant central nucleus. The resolution of the nucleus into stars cannot be seen on this photograph.* (*Mount Wilson Observatory.*)

PLATE 41. *The outer whorls of the Andromeda galaxy; two spiral arms are seen, as well as patches of brilliant hot stars, and evidences of obscuration.* (*Mount Wilson Observatory.*)

PLATE 42. *The spiral galaxy Messier 51, seen almost face-on. (Mount Wilson Observatory.)*

PLATE 43. *The spiral galaxy N.G.C. 4565 (No. 4565 in the "New General Catalogue" of galaxies, nebulae, and clusters), seen nearly edge-on. (Palomar Observatory.)*

PLATE 44. *The elliptical galaxy N.G.C. 147, one of the small companions of the Andromeda galaxy.* (*Palomar Observatory.*)

PLATE 45. *The Magellanic Clouds, companions of our own galaxy. The bright star in the foreground is Achernar, in the constellation Eridanus. (Boyden Station, Harvard Observatory.)*

PLATE 46. *The Large Magellanic Cloud (compare Plates 45 and 48).* (*Boyden Station, Harvard Observatory.*)

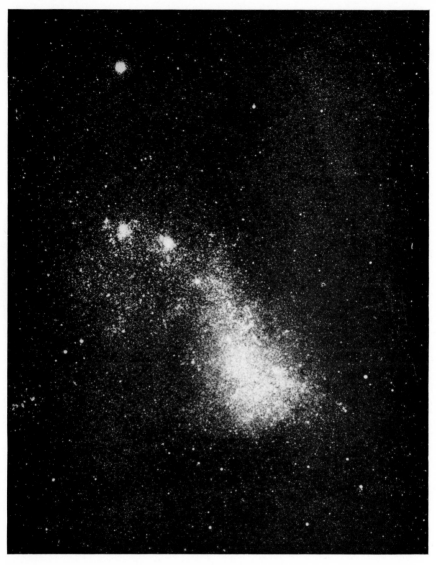

PLATE 47. *The Small Magellanic Cloud.* The scale is larger than for Plate 46 (compare Plate 45). (*Boyden Station, Harvard Observatory.*)

PLATE 48. *The central part of the Large Magellanic Cloud. Notice the "Tarantula" nebula, and the rich display of bright nebulae, clusters, and dark markings.* (B. J. Bok, Harvard-Armagh-Dunsink telescope, Boyden Station, Harvard Observatory.)

PLATE 49. *A small, faint, irregular galaxy, seen through the constellation Sextans. (Palomar Observatory.)*

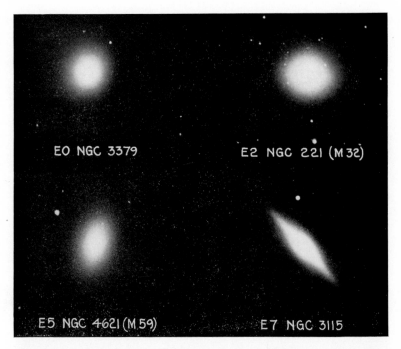

PLATE 50. *Four typical elliptical galaxies. N.G.C. 221 is one of the companions of the Andromeda spiral. (Mount Wilson Observatory.)*

PLATE 51. *The elliptical galaxy N.G.C. 205, a companion of the Andromeda galaxy; the photograph is on a red-sensitive plate, and shows the resolution into stars. (Baade, Palomar Observatory.)*

PLATE 52. *The giant elliptical galaxy Messier 87, surrounded by an aura of globular clusters, which look like hazy stars in the photograph. A few more distant galaxies are also visible. (Palomar Observatory.)*

PLATE 53. *The spiral galaxy in Triangulum, Messier 33.* (*Mount Wilson Observatory.*)

PLATE 54. *The spiral galaxy N.G.C. 2403.* (*Mount Wilson Observatory.*)

PLATE 55. *The spiral galaxy Messier 63.* (*Mount Wilson Observatory.*)

PLATE 56. *The spiral galaxy Messier 83.* (*Harvard Observatory.*)

PLATE 57. *The spiral galaxy N.G.C. 2903.* (*Mount Wilson Observatory.*)

PLATE 58. *The spiral galaxy Messier 64.* (*Mount Wilson Observatory.*)

PLATE 59. *The spiral galaxy N.G.C. 7217.* (*Mount Wilson Observatory.*)

PLATE 60. *The barred spiral galaxy N.G.C. 4314. (Mount Wilson Observatory.)*

PLATE 61. *The barred spiral galaxy N.G.C. 7741. Note the resemblance to the Large Magellanic Cloud. (Mount Wilson Observatory.)*

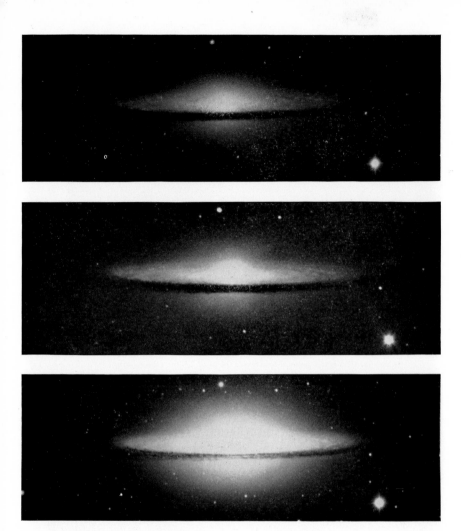

PLATE 62. *The spiral galaxy N.G.C. 4594, in ultraviolet light (above), blue light (middle), and red light (below). The difference of distribution in the three colors is clearly marked, and shows that the brightest red stars (Population II) have a more nearly spherical distribution than the bluer stars. (Baade, Mount Wilson Observatory.)*

PLATE 63. *The spiral galaxy Messier 81.* (*Mount Wilson Observatory.*)

PLATE 64. *The small irregular galaxy N.G.C. 2796, a companion of Messier 81. This picture is on a much larger scale than Plate 63.*

PLATE 65. *The peculiar galaxy N.G.C. 4038–4039, difficult to fit into the series of galactic forms. (Harvard Observatory.)*

PLATE 66. *The enigmatic object N.G.C. 5128. It emits intense radio waves. Opinion is divided as to whether it is within our galaxy or a distant system. (Harvard Observatory.)*

PLATE 67. *Part of the great Coma cluster of galaxies.* (*Palomar Observatory.*)